" ... A SMALL MIRACLE HAPPENS

between the time I awake in the morning and the time I leave the apartment. I wake up ugly. And when I leave—how do I say this? —I'm not so bad. When I go to parties I don't stand around wondering what makes so-and-so so marvelous looking; I look just fine . . . But all of this is learned."

. . . and it all started once upon a time when an ugly 15-year-old decided to become a swan. She did it herself and made the grade in spades. Here's the inside story of Barbara Johns Waterston, now a glamorous fashion photographer with a gift of beauty for you . . .

Other SIGNET Books You'll Find Useful

PULL
YOURSELF
TOGETHER

OR, HOW TO LOOK MARVELOUS
ON NEXT TO NOTHING

---

by Barbara Johns Waterston

DECORATIONS BY ISADORE SELTZER

A SIGNET BOOK

Published by
THE NEW AMERICAN LIBRARY

SIGNET TRADEMARK REG. U.S. PAT. OFF. AND FOREIGN COUNTRIES
REGISTERED TRADEMARK—MARCA REGISTRADA
HECHO EN CHICAGO, U.S.A.

*SIGNET BOOKS are published by
The New American Library, Inc.,
1301 Avenue of the Americas, New York, New York 10019*

PRINTED IN THE UNITED STATES OF AMERICA

To Sam

CONTENTS

1

n Making It

◆ When I was fifteen my ugly-duckling sister went and did an awful thing—she turned into a swan. It happened so suddenly. I had been talking on the phone with my hero of the hour (he had called, I had answered, and naturally I assumed he wanted to speak with me), and after a painful five minutes of adolescent conversation he asked to speak to her! And then he asked her out! You can imagine my chagrin. I was forced to notice that she had lost all her baby fat and looked like a fourteen-year-old Grace Kelly. It was awful.

Then I went into the bathroom—I'll never forget it—and had a hard look in the mirror. Saw a lot of things I didn't want to see. My nose, for instance. It was fat. All the thirty thousand

9

freckles sat on pasty white skin. My ears? Not only was one higher than the other—the left one turned in and the right one out. My hair was kinky, not curly. My eyes were tiny and, at that point, red. My chin stuck out like some kind of a buttress. My eyebrows were skimpy, my eyelashes sparse, and my mouth was plain too big.

I didn't like what I saw that night. But as I look back, that was the moment when I began the search for an attractive me.

I splashed cold water on my face and decided to pull myself together. I wasn't going to give up, not then—I was only fifteen. I'd fight. If I didn't make it, I'd fake it.

Well, I have some theories:

◈ ANY WOMAN WHO ISN'T GREAT LOOKING JUST DOESN'T WANT TO BE . . .

Polly would walk around looking like a slob on purpose. (Polly's a friend of mine.) She had this idea that it was superficial to care about the way she looked. She told herself she had too many other things to think about. But the facts are, she wasted so much time justifying herself that most of those "important thoughts" were simply that she was *not* going to be superficial, she was *not* going to waste her time on her person, she was going to think about important things, and so on.

Once I heard her telling someone, ". . . I don't care; it's too much effort. If people don't like me

10

the way I am, then . . ." She never finished her sentence.

Polly didn't care because she didn't dare care. Looking your best is like making a public statement: "Hello, world, I like you and I want to please you." What if they *still* didn't like her? At least now she could say, "I don't care." If she went and ironed her dresses and put a little something on her face to help along her bland features, people wouldn't believe her when she said she didn't care.

◆ OR SHE WANTS TO TOO MUCH . . .

Then, of course, there's Ellen. (Ellen's another friend.) If Ellen has a cold and the directions say take two pills every three hours, then Ellen takes four. Twice as good, right? She puts her makeup on like that. If three drops of foundation do it, how much better half the bottle. Right? Ellen tries too hard, and that's worse than not trying at all. Ellen's desperate.

◆ OR SHE JUST DOESN'T KNOW THE SCORE . . .

Most girls are like Nancy. Nancy cared, and she wasn't desperate; she just didn't know what she was doing. Like she'd go ahead and buy the hip skirt, but she'd let it hang below her knees. And she'd wonder why hip skirts looked so much better on Sally. She just didn't know the score. She didn't open her eyes.

The reason for this book is very simple: I know you can "make it" on as little time and money as you are spending now. I know, because I made it for a long time on sixty-five dollars a week. It's not *what* you do, it's *how*. And it's not only *how* you do it, but when. I mean when do you wash your hair? The night after you have to or the night before? When do you sew the button on your coat? One night a week when you do all your sewing, or in the taxi on the way to the show? When do you worry about your eyebrows? In the ladies' room of the restaurant, or before your date picks you up? What are you thinking about when you bump smack into your Mr. Wonderful on the street? What he's saying, or whether your slip is showing?

I know how you feel, believe me. There was a time when I, too, thought it a sacrilege to powder my nose or straighten my hair. That was tampering with God's very blessings. What right had I to paint my fingernails shiny if in the beginning they were dull? It just didn't seem honest. Black was black and white was white, and painted dolls were painted dolls.

And what's worse, everyone agreed. "Models may look well in pictures, but you should see them in real life," they would say. "They take their makeup off with chisels." Or, "Yeah, but they scare their husbands at night. There aren't any faces beneath all that war paint." Oh, I was convinced. Every so often I'd stick a clip in my hair at night—that was acceptable. And I'd smear some bright red gunk on my mouth. That, too, was all right where I grew up. But if hems hung, they hung. It was because my hips were too small. It was my fault. If my nose shined, it shined. But it was "me."

I've changed. Now I know that even if there is such a thing as a "natural beauty"—and I have my definite doubts—she is only a natural beauty naked. The minute she gets up and puts something on, she can do it wrong. She can comb her hair wrong. She can wear the wrong shoe, or something as dumb as the wrong glove. She and her mistakes can get in the way of her natural beauty.

You can change, too, with a little concentration and planning. The first thing to do is admit you can't go it alone. You need the help of three.

◈ First find a hairdresser you can trust. You have to know that you can walk in there almost any time of any day and he'll squeeze you in somehow, no matter how busy he is. And that when you walk out you won't walk out looking "done." This in itself is a job. It will probably take many a trip to many a different salon. At the last minute, when you see he's about to go too far with the teasing and goo, you may have to look at your watch and say, "Good Lord! I was supposed to meet my sister ten minutes ago!" And then run out. (Don't go back.) This doesn't mean you'll be spending each morning in the beauty parlor before going to work. You can't afford the money, and you can't afford the time either. But a good hairdresser, even if you get him only once every two or three months, is a moral support that is terribly important. I never realized how heavily I depended on mine until he had to leave town. I hadn't been in to see him in over two months, but as soon as I got wind he was gone, my hair began throwing temper tantrums.

◈ Next find a good cleaner. Good luck! It may take months. (And it may mean a few juicy fights.) Let him know you expect his complete devotion. I had vicious arguments with mine for the longest time. Now, finally, he's doing what he should always have done . . . like sewing buttons back on when they fall off during cleaning. Like delivering at eight in the morning when he says eight in the morning. Like having a look first and screaming second when I complain that a blouse is missing. Cleaners can be bullies. You have to show them you mean business. Big business if they play ball.

◈ The third, the last, is the hardest to find. A little old lady or a little old man who can sew. Not a frustrated designer who thinks he or she knows what you want better than you do. Just a sweet soul who follows directions and doesn't expect the shirt off your back in return.

But excluding these—your dedicated hairdresser, your devoted cleaner, your dear little seamstress—excluding these, you're on your own.

Really on your own. Don't listen to anyone. Even your best friend isn't your best friend if you're a threat. Mothers, too. Don't listen.

14

Mothers mean well, but they all want their girls to look like virgins. And men? Men just don't know what they like. A fashion-editor friend of mine was dating a doctor-type who was against "chic" in every way, or so he thought. So she, the fool, stopped lining her eyes and teasing her hair. He stopped seeing her. No, you've got to do it yourself. If you don't, no one will. You've got to decide who you are and then be it.

All I can tell you is that a small miracle happens between the time I awake in the morning and the time I leave the apartment. I wake up ugly. And when I leave—how do I say this?—I'm not so bad. When I go to parties I don't stand around wondering what makes so-and-so so marvelous looking; I look just fine. I can think about other things!

But all this is learned. Those unfortunate features I saw in the mirror that night at fifteen I still see. Every morning. What I've learned to do is change the things I can change and like the things I can't.

I'm not saying dowdiness is a dread disease, but I do think it's a symptom. In her book, *The Neurotic's Notebook*, Mike McLaughlin says, " 'Pull yourself together' is seldom said to anyone who can." I don't think she's right.

2

n Closets

◆ My cousin Alex was a happy-go-lucky, sort of take-things-as-they-come kind of girl, with the messiest closets you ever saw. She was always a little at loose ends, but that never bothered her much. Not until one Wednesday morning . . .

This Wednesday morning she had a 9:30 interview with a Mr. Garrison, creative director of an important ad agency. The job open was an "art buyer," and Alex was qualified. Besides, she had been strongly recommended by someone in a strong enough position to strongly recommend with strength. It was virtually wrapped up, this job, even before the interview. Alex knew it. Not only that, but she had checked around and learned that Mr. Garrison was one perfect boss, his only bugaboo being punctuality.

She had set her alarm for 8 o'clock. Half hour to get up, exercise and eat, half hour to put her makeup on and dress, half hour to get there. And at 8 o'clock she did get up. By 8:50 she was all through with her shower, her makeup, her exercises, and her grapefruit and coffee. Absolutely no sweat. All she had to do now was put on her dress. She was ten minutes earlier than expected.

She went to the closet, put on her black wool dress, and had a look in the mirror. Great mustard spot in the front. Okay, she'd wear the gray one. Tried *it* on; the hem was out in the back. Damn! Okay, the beige shift. Where was it? Oh yes, there it was, under the plaid dress. No, torn under the arm. And so on, until finally at 9:20 she left her apartment in the original black dress with the hopes she could hide the spot by holding her bag there.

She blew her lunch money on a cab but, even so, arrived fifteen minutes late for Mr. Garrison. Traffic. She didn't get the job. But she cleaned out her closet that night.

◆ There's something a little icky about the whole idea of messy closets, anyway. I keep thinking dirty underwear and run-down shoes. It's impossible to be well-dressed if everything's crammed and chaotic in your closet.

American women goggle at the chic that European women seem to come by naturally. How they can look fantastic Every Day. How it's the rule, not the occasional mistake. I say it has to do with clean closets. Last year I was in Rome for a week, and I went daily to an outdoor café for coffee and those little sandwiches you get in outdoor cafés. And daily I saw a pretty Italian girl, no more than nineteen or twenty, looking like a million dollars. Every day (for seven days) this Italian girl wore the very same black suit. I'll bet *her* closet wasn't a mess. I'll bet every night she went home she took cleaning fluid to the collar of her only black suit, checked the hem, hung it up, and had only to choose between pull-overs in the morning. And maybe scarves.

When I was in prep school there was a girl named Christine Smith, and she was the best-dressed girl in the school, see. It was a known fact. Everyone always talked about it behind her back, how great her clothes were, how wealthy her family must be. Then one day I was in her room and I peeked in her closet: three dresses, one suit, two skirts, seven tops, four pairs of shoes. Period. They were lined up according to category with the hangers going in the same direction, one inch apart as in small specialty shops after six. The buttons were buttoned, the zippers zipped. Each of the shoes (hanging in a shoe bag, of course) had a shine that glistened. She was the best-dressed girl in that school and possibly the best lesson I learned there.

◈ Cleaning out your closet seems like an impossible undertaking, I know, but all you have to do is begin.

Begin at the five-and-dime some Saturday

18

afternoon when the prospects for Saturday night look grim. A closet-clean is good for the psyche. And anyway, it's going to take longer than you think. You don't want to be interrupted.

At the five-and-dime buy a skirt hanger that will hang six skirts. Buy twenty plastic hangers. Buy a shoe bag and six pairs of shoe trees. (If you have more than six pairs of shoes, buy accordingly.) Buy a belt hanger. If there are shelves in your closet, then buy shelf paper too. If you want to get jazzy, you can even buy a big chunk of cork for hanging all your costume jewelry.

All right, you're ready. It's Saturday night with nowhere to go, and you're standing in front of your closet looking bewildered. Don't just stand there—dig in. Take everything in there out of there and throw it on the bed. Get into the corners with the vacuum cleaner. Spray some moth stuff around. By now your closet is disgustingly clean. After you've lined the shelves, if there are shelves, you're ready to start putting things back in.

Are you? Wait a minute. Think for a minute. Think of your closet as a kind of garden—you have to get rid of the weeds to give the flowers air.

So if you haven't worn it happily in the past year, chuck it. Or fix it. "It" is that dress, skirt, suit, whatever you've been hanging on to because your mother once told you a willful waste was a woeful want. Forget it. If you're saving it for a rainy day, I predict rainy days ahead. My dean told us at graduation, "Don't read good books. There isn't time. Read only the great ones." I say, "Don't wear 'good' clothes. You're young! Wear only the great ones." That's what I say. And don't hang on to it because you think it might come back into style. It won't. Fashion may borrow from the past, but it never returns. Believe me, when it's gone, it's gone. Like old boy friends. So get rid of last year's suit if that's what it looks like.

But maybe it just needs shortening. Don't throw away a perfectly good skirt because it's too long. If you know that nothing will fix it, however, get rid of it. Give it to the cleaning woman. No room for weeds in your garden.

Start trying on in front of a full-length mirror. (If you haven't a full-length mirror, you're not well-dressed.) Try on every single dress and look. Take an honest look. Here's where it's hard, because women (and men) have this thing about deceiving themselves. Does that sixteenth-of-an-inch droop in the back of your favorite black dress really matter? Yes! It's the difference between almost making it and making it, that's all. If *you* notice it, they'll notice it.

While you're trying on these clothes, you should experiment with different accessories. A scarf that you never dreamed would go with a particular dress may not have, three months ago. But that was three months ago. The old rule that dots didn't go with checks? How quickly that was shattered when someone with a little guts decided it didn't look bad at all. Stand there like a model and try maybe every scarf you own with every dress. And every top with every skirt. And everything with every shoe. You'll find your three marvelous dresses and your one marvelous suit have turned into sixteen different looks.

Only you can judge what's great. But if it's not great, and there isn't much chance of it ever being great, I repeat: get rid of it.

At the end of this try-on session you'll probably wind up with very few clothes in the closet. The floor, on the other hand, will be heaped—a pile to be altered, a pile to be cleaned, and a huge pile of giveaways.

Don't let that scare you—it's fine. Really. It's a good sign. Just make sure that everything that goes into that closet from here on in is perfect. *Really* ready-to-wear. (What we call ready-to-wear in this country is a joke. Nothing's ready-to-wear. If a skirt fits at the hips, that doesn't mean it fits. It may hang two inches below the knee, and in fact probably does, unless you're a giraffe. I'm 5′8″ tall and I've never bought anything, ever, that didn't need shortening. Even what the manufacturers call mini-skirts are what I call "old-lady," right off the rack.) Just because it's new doesn't mean it's ready to hang in your beautiful flower closet.

While you're at it, weed out your bureau drawers. I'm all for sectioning them. Line them at least with paper, perhaps even a cheery cotton held down with staples or double-edged tape. Throw in some pretty sachets. They make your clean clothes cleaner somehow. If you still have time, clean out your desk. Hell, clean out everything. Your purse. Your pantry. Your medicine cabinet. You're cleaning out your soul. Get rid of the "stuff" that has been exhausting you all these months, that you never use and you know you never will, that only gets in the way. This editing-out-everything process should happen once every three months. By the way, I wouldn't have things altered at the end of a season—like your woolens in April—because chances are the proportions will have changed by the following September. Send them to the cleaners and have him store them until then. Last season's clothes are temporary weeds.

Come Monday morning when you've dropped off the cleaning at the cleaners, the altering at the seamstress, and left the give-aways for the cleaning woman, you're going to feel so incredibly free. Like *you're* in charge now. You're taking life for the ride. Excess "stuff" isn't hanging you up. Congratulations. You've taken the biggest step. Everything else is peanuts now.

P.S. Wednesday, when the cleaning comes back, remove the plastic garment bags before you hang those flowers up. They're not going to get dusty, because nothing goes in there that you won't be wearing often. Right? Plastic bags are excess baggage, just like those weeds.

3

On Clothes

◈ In this crazy age of the Cheetah, of the yé-yé girl, of everything *à go-go*, anything goes. It's true. Your negligee may well be made of ermine. You can wear leather to a black-tie dinner party and organdy to the office and pants for cocktails and get away with it. My point here is that gravy is gravy, and meat is meat, and gravy's rather thin without the meat; so if you're on a budget, buy the meat first. Don't get a vinyl skirt until you first have a wool one. Get me?

So now I'm going to give you a meat list—a basic wardrobe that will prepare you for anything. A spur-of-the-moment trip around the world, anything. You fill in with the gravy when you can afford to.

But I have a thought or two before I begin.

23

America's the land of instant coffee, frozen foods, and automatic washing machines, and that's all grand, but it's the only land I've visited (actually I live here) where women think they can walk into a store, buy a dress, and walk out chic—"instant chic." Well, there's no such animal. Fashion is not a specific dress, a specific color, a specific designer or fabric. Fashion is proportion, that's what fashion is. You can look dowdy in a Rudi Gernreich dress if you try hard enough. I'll never forget seeing a rich Park Avenue type a few years back walking her dog wearing a Courreges dress. She had been one of the first to buy Courreges, and I'm sure she felt pretty "up-to-date." Trouble was, she missed the whole point. Courreges is proportion, and she had lengthened her Courreges to way below her knees. And what, after all, is Courreges without the knee?

Thought number two is this: forget about the four seasons. Manufacturers add seasons like "resort" and "holiday" onto the standard four as a gimmick to psych you into buying even more. When you're on a no-gravy type budget, there are only two seasons and they are summer and winter. I'm twenty-six years old, and the last time I had a spring coat was when I was eight, and I wore it on Easter Sunday and never again because right after Easter it turned hot that year and the next year it was too small. A spring coat is in the gravy category, as far as I'm concerned. Fine if you have sixty dollars to throw away. Even if there is a spring, it only lasts two weeks, and for two weeks you can jolly well wear your raincoat.

Okay, I think we're ready. Here's your meat list:

◆ LONG EVENING DRESS

Leave the elegance to the old ladies. A long evening dress is nice enough, but it's gravy. You don't need one unless you're making your debut in Vienna or something like that. On the whole you can wear a short dress almost anywhere. If you don't dare, make an evening skirt and wear one of your own silk blouses. Evening skirts are so simple to make I even made one once. Just take some good heavy fabric (so you don't have to line it—drapery fabric is very good), sew a seam up the back, throw on a waistband, a few snaps and hooks (don't bother with a zipper—that's too much like work), and you've got it made. If you muck up the waist, never mind. You can always wear a sash or wear a pull-over pulled over. Culottes are gravy too.

◆ COCKTAIL DRESSES

Two of them. You need one inoffensive, almost dignified dress for engagement parties and wedding receptions. Notice I say "almost dignified." Don't go and get really dignified. Because it's at the engagement parties and weddings that you want to really shine. You have to be deliciously single and independent, not spinsterly, not like yesterday's newspaper. If married, look glad to be married, not ragged from diapers and formula.

But do not be obvious. I think the trick is to buy just a standard conservative dress and wear it an inch too short. That will add the spice.

I've had mine for going on eight years now. I bought ahead of a trend, bought a waistless dress with a sash while they were still hung up on the princess lines. When the Empire look came in, I wore the sash below the bust. When the cowboy look hit, I wore it at the hip. Every year I shorten it. It's still my favorite dress.

This dress shouldn't be black because it's not very correct to wear black at weddings and engagements. But keep it dark; and if you buy silk, then you can wear it year round.

Make up for your caution with the other. This dress should be a show-stopper. The neckline needn't come down to the navel, but it can. (What's modest for some isn't modest for others. What's modest, anyway? It's whatever you can get away with. Some women look obscene in a sleeveless dress. Others don't. Still others look "modest" in a bikini.) Fall in love with this dress. Put a dollar down and think it over for a day or two. If you feel the same way the second time around, then you'll probably feel that way whenever you wear it. I'd get black, but that's up to you.

◈ OFFICE DRESSES

Three. Be picky about the cut of your dresses. What's going on at the shoulder? Does the seam go straight up from under the arm? That's good. Or does it curve around so the sleeve starts below the shoulder? That's bad. Are there no darts? That's good. Or do the darts point straight out so you look like a pyramid that's on its ear. That's bad. Does it hang straight and waistless from the armpits? That's good. Or is the hourglass shape built in? That's bad. If your dress comes with a belt to match, two things: cut off the little belt loops as soon as you can get to some scissors— they're hick. And don't wear the belt that came with the dress unless it's quality. (They're usually plastic, or plastic-backed, and horrid.) Don't fret that a new belt may not match; think tone and contrasts, not color. (I have one of those black leather spaghetti-thin sashes that tie and I wear it with every dress that needs a belt.)

The only other major don't is slits and kick pleats. They date the dress to at least seven years ago, even though you may have bought it last week. They are easy enough to get rid of, so there's no excuse not to. But have it done professionally. It only costs a couple of dollars. (A good rule is to allow $5 for alterations whenever you buy a dress.)

◆ SUITS

One. Dark. One day last spring my friend Marge got up, had breakfast, etc., and put on her dark suit. She met with her copy chief at 9:30 and was well turned out for that appointment. During the day she went to two fashion shows, had lunch with a friend, went to an ad meeting, and she couldn't have been dressed more appropriately. After work she went to a fancy cocktail party where there were diamonds and things all over the place—just fine. From there (without the time or the inclination to go home and change) she went to the New York-Detroit game at Yankee Stadium. And when the game was finished, she stopped off at an after-dinner party (the newest kind of New York party). I guess I don't have to tell you that her dark suit worked well there too.

Aren't many places you can't go in a dark suit. I've even heard it rumored that Coco Chanel once turned up at some black-tie something or other honoring some ambassador or other in a black suit. So you never know.

The important thing to watch for when you go to get your suit is the jacket. (The skirt follows the same rules as all skirts. See below.) Look at the shoulders. The collar. Does it stand away a little from the neck? It should. Does it have shoulder pads? It shouldn't. Any plastic and/or rhinestone buttons? Good grief. Does it grip the waist like a girdle? Don't buy it. Does it have a lot going on? It won't leave room for play. Is the jacket too short? Too long? (Hip length is hip.) Is the jacket too bulky? You'll never get your coat on.

It boils down to this: your dark suit is the most important thing you own, the thing you may wear as often as three times a week. And you know you'll get only what you pay for. So pay. Go without a telephone—I did until my raise came through, and that was eight months later. (Your dates can call you at the office.) Bring your lunch to work. Type a thesis for your would-be doctor friend, and send him a bill. If all else fails, charge it. (I'm for living a little above your means, anyway. It's modern.)

◆ PANTS SUIT

One. In New York City a pants suit is meat, not gravy. And I would think that by next year the same will be true in Chicago, it's so cold there. Los Angeles is turning swinging, and a pants suit, although not meat, is gravy with giblets. It's not a must but definitely a plus, if you know what I mean. I have my doubts whether stuffy San Francisco will ever get the message. I'm afraid a pants suit is just very thin gravy there, what with all that Culture. They're still all wearing long evening dresses in San Francisco.

The only thing to remember when you buy a pants suit is that the jacket should be very long, long enough to hide your big rear-end. (And if your rear-end is really big, forget pants suits, okay?) And the pants should be long enough. Unfortunately pants suit manufacturers don't understand this—they're still making pants that end above the ankle bone. (Remember, long pants look like long legs.) Great for traveling in airplanes, unbeatable for football games, and fun for discothequing.

◆ SKIRTS

Three. One gray, one navy or beige, one tweed or check. Again, why the no-color? Because a skirt shouldn't be a focal point. A skirt is a foundation, so to speak. It's a base from which to work. It shouldn't draw attention; it should carry the attention. Being on the bottom, skirts should look heavier than the tops.

Never let skirts cup under your rump. You have to have room to walk. Not like a Japanese— I mean walk! The test is whether you can climb the steps of an Egyptian pyramid in it. Maybe you haven't ever seen an Egyptian pyramid. Well, they're big. Each step is about mid-thigh to crotch level. Could you take a step that big in your skirt? If you can, then the skirt is probably okay. (But don't stock up on these square-dancing dirndls; they're for squares.) You can get the same effect with godets, pleats, or simply some soft gathering under the waistband.

◈ RAINCOAT
One. Beige and boring. Phooey on the flowery little shower-curtain raincoats made out of silk taffeta. I'll bet women who wear them have princess telephones. And pretty television sets. Tricky little metal designs on their air conditioners. Some things just shouldn't be pretty, and raincoats fall into that category. "Pretty" raincoats are like artificial flowers—the prettier they are, the uglier they are, if you know what I mean. I feel the same about vinyl; anyway, it makes you sweat.

◈ WINTER COAT
One. By now you probably think of me as super-conservative. But believe me, no one who knows

me has ever accused me of that. I'm not a Republican. I don't think women should stay home and just take care of their babies if they want more. I believe in affairs if they're good—all those things. But I still say buy a no-color coat. Beige, which goes with anything, or black, which goes anywhere.

◆ THEATER COAT
Get one eventually—you really do need one. If you get it in silk you can wear it spring, summer, and fall. Occasionally I even wore mine in the dead of winter and had my date bring the taxi right to the door so I didn't catch cold. If it's really much too cold, wear your pea jacket.

◆ PEA JACKET
Which brings us to the pea jacket. It's straight out of the Army-Navy store, this decade's car coat. Wear it with slacks, with a skirt and sweater, over one or all of your office dresses, and, if it's really cold, instead of your theater coat. It's navy and double-breasted and very, very warm.

◆ SWEATERS
Five. Three poor-boy and two shetlands. (The girls in Paris are wearing shetlands now—with kilts.) Anyway, shetlands are always good in the country, and poor-boys are sexy. Buy the colors that go with your hair. No mohair—mohair's had it. Anyway, it tickles your nose. And we won't even talk about angora.

◆ T SHIRTS and TANK TOPS

Four T shirts and four tank tops. Susan's a photographer, and she's terrific. On a Monday we photographed down at the beach. Susan met us in blue jeans and an old faded red T shirt— the kind your kid brother plays softball in. She looked like a slob, but it was a great-looking slob standing there, if you know what I mean. She had work to do, and these were her work clothes. That was Monday. On Wednesday, when she brought the contacts over to my office, there she was in a fantastic bone twill coat and skirt she had picked up in Paris. And under the coat? On top of the skirt? That same grubby T shirt! Wait, it gets worse! On that grubby red T shirt she had stuck a Cartier gold pin, yet. And she looked marvelous. Susan has that sixth sense; she knows that she can do whatever she wants and get away with it.

T shirts have stepped up from the uniform for runny-nosed children they were ten years ago. Now everyone wears them. I do. All over—to business appointments, to the beach, sailing, shopping. Almost anywhere during the day. Same with tank tops, only they go with everything in the evening too.

◆ OXFORD BUTTON-DOWN SHIRTS

Two. Everyone should have two of these even though they're so dull. They're good in the country under shetland sweaters with tweed skirts or slacks. (But don't get the fake button-downs—the feminized ones with teeny-weeny collars and then the buttons. Or worse, the rounded collars with the buttons.) If you get button-down shirts at all, get them just like your husband's. Or your boy friend's. Your brother's? If there aren't pockets on the chest, they come from Brooks Brothers. They last six years.

❖ BLOUSES
Two long-sleeved classic off-white silk blouses. Expensive—at least twelve dollars each. Not fake silk, real silk. You can wear these to the office on casual days with a gray flannel skirt and leather belt. You can wear them with your long evening skirt, entertaining at home, or for dinner out. They last forever.

❖ BLUE JEANS or FRONTIER PANTS
One pair, corduroy or denim. When I invited Valerie to my "paint-my-apartment" party, she replied, "Great. I can mess up my new blue jeans." Blue jeans are like sneakers. The first time you wear them they're just awful. You want to go roll in the mud or something. Like paint a friend's apartment. (But dunking them in Clorox doesn't do it; they don't look faded and grubby —they look like they've been dunked in Clorox.)

❖ SHORT SHORTS
One pair. Get some if your legs are good.

❖ BERMUDAS
One pair. Get some if they're not.

33

◈ SLIPS

Two half and two full, a black and white of each. By full slip I mean with a top on it, not a full-full, down-to-your-toes. In fact, what I really mean is a half-full slip. One of those demi-tasse chemises that fall just past the tops of your stockings. The wonderful reason for having one of these is that possibly you won't be wearing a bra, yet you want something separating you from your clothes-clothes. The awful reason is that you may still be wearing see-through nylon blouses. Ouch.

◈ BRAS

Three white bras and one black. (Don't wear your white ones under your black dresses; they won't stay white for long.) Padded bras are out. Pointed bras are out. Bosoms are out, for that matter, but they're on their way back in. There are two kinds of bosoms—the grapefruit kind and the banana kind. For both of these, the way I see it, there's only one kind of bra. (Now how do I say "flattening" without all of you getting hysterical? Maybe I should say "soft"—or "subtle.") Anyway, it should have tucks, not darts. It should curve gently, not point. There should be little mounds, not mountains. The only answer is teen-age bras or Rudi Gernreich's "no-bra." I can not understand why lingerie manu-facturers insist that to be American you have to look like Jayne Mansfield. If you ever get to Paris, there's where to buy your underwear.

◈ GIRDLES

One white, one black. I don't believe much in girdles, though sometimes I wear them. The whole idea of girdles is kind of disgusting. I don't blame men for hating them. (How would you like your man to wear a truss? Gick.) Simply figure out where the bulge is and buy accordingly. There are no chic girdles.

◈ PANTS

Four white, four black. You don't want to rinse out your undies every night. That's so sort of Y.W.C.A. (I heard a marvelous story about Ziegfeld, the great man behind the 1930 Ziegfeld Follies. Every time he hired a new girl he would give her fifty dollars to go and spend on whatever she wanted in the most lavish lingerie shop in New York. The audience never saw what she bought, but *she* knew. She knew that what she was wearing underneath her costume was even sexier than the costume. It showed in her face, on stage. Smart man, Mr. Ziegfeld. He knew women better than a lot of women know women.) Oh, and have you tried those new bikini pants? They're quite marvelous. It's hard to describe . . . it's the slight sensation of elastic across the hip bone. Makes you feel skinny, somehow. You want to stretch. To dance. It's true. They don't bind at the waist, don't bunch under girdles. Anyway, if you haven't tried them, try them.

◈ GARTER BELTS

I wish someone in the garter-belt business would

realize what's happened to this world of ours and design a garter belt that doesn't hang down to the knees. Skirts are getting shorter every minute, no matter what Paris is trying to tell us. But stockings are still too short, and garter belts are still too long. I've almost given up on garter belts and resorted to little panty girdles, even though I hate them.

◈ STOCKINGS
I wear the fish-net ones now because they're the only ones long enough. And they don't run. Or panty-hose. In the summer I use Quick-Tan.

◈ BODY STOCKING
Overrated. And obscene. There, I said it. Why do you want to wear a body stocking? Because it's sexy? Well, I don't think there's a thing sexy about them. Neither does Sam. Because you don't want to wear a bra? So don't wear a bra! Anyway, what do you do when nature calls?

◈ NIGHTGOWNS
Two. I think I'll stay out of this. It's up to you. You can even get pajamas if you want to.

◈ BATHROBE
Two. One of mine is terry cloth for after showers. The other is long, to the floor, and very feminine. Nice for breakfast.

◈ BOX OF BAND-AIDS and/or STRAPLESS BRA
One. Or you can hoist a half slip up to There and wear it like a bathing-suit top.

◆ SHOES

Four pairs. Maybe we can blame it on Jackie Kennedy, I don't know. Maybe it's just the inevitable making itself evident. But the world has changed. Cinderella, with her itsy-bitsy foot, is just a laughing matter today. Today the girl with size-eight or -nine foot is going to get the prince. So if you are size nine or ten, don't fight it. Don't squeeze into a seven. When your feet hurt, it shows in your face. And anyway, big feet make your legs look thinner.

Which brings up to the leg. The foot is an extension of the leg. Something with which to walk. Stride. Get it? In other words, like skirts, shoes should allow you to walk. With comfort. Ease. That's why the low-heeled walking shoes. If you buy those four-inch spikes of yesteryear, no comfort at all. And a turned-up toe is what happens. Lots of angles that don't relate to each other. The foot, instead of being that extension, is a distortion.

Here's where you spend your money. When you go out to buy shoes, don't pinch pennies. You'll end up pinching your toes. And pinched toes lead to corns, and corns lead to embarrassment when you take your shoes off. Don't pinch the pennies even if the shoe fits. A cheap shoe is a cheap shoe. As Geri says (and Geri knows what she's doing—she's the publicity director of a good store in New York at the ripe age of twenty-six), "You're right if your leather is right." Your handbag (we'll get to that in a minute) and your shoes really tell the tale. I

37

mean, picture it: A tall, attractive girl in a beige Chanel suit, a good-looking silk blouse, her hair all straight and marvelous, her stockings pale and proper, her makeup not even showing—there she is, looking like a million, and . . . and she's carrying a plastic bag, wearing plastic shoes to match. Could you die?

The five-dollar shoe may even wear as long as the thirty-dollar shoe, but the whole time you're wearing it, you're wishing it would wear out so you can buy another pair.

Play around with your shoes. Wear patent leather in the winter, for instance. (By the way, the only sure way I've found for cleaning patent leather is good old-fashioned spit. Spit plus Kleenex do amazing things. There may be a more up-to-date solution to the patent cleaning problem, but I'm sick of ruining good shoes to find it. Vaseline? No. Neutral-color shoe polish? No. Vinegar? No. Spit.)

About style, all I can tell you is that I've never yet owned a pair a shoes that's gone out of fashion. They wear out first. Right now the trend is either the big clunky clodhopper (the "Gucci" shoe, for example) you wear with heavy stockings or the very sexy little French or Italian sling-backs with low vamps that reveal a little toe (almost as effective as a low-cut dress). No "pumps," they're neither side of the fence. Get some brown clunkers, and some black, some beige, and whatever-other-color sexy ones.

Your evening shoes? Black. Silk. Expensive.

Sexy. You can wear them with every dressy dress you own. Girls who run around having white satin shoes dyed to match particular dresses are going to so much unnecessary time and trouble. Fact is, that whole matchy-poo look has had it.

◈ LOAFERS
One pair. Everybody needs a pair of loafers. What if you're invited to the country for the weekend? Then what do you do? Run around looking smart-city in your black pumps? Loafers can go anywhere flats can go, and often they go better. So forget about flats unless you're loaded or unless you already have a pair.

I've had my loafers since I was seventeen. They're brown.

◈ RUBBER SANDALS
One pair. It's an attitude, this whole thing. If you're well-dressed ever, you're well-dressed every day. Every minute. If you "make it," you make it even in the bathtub. You don't go to sleep with grit between your toes is what I'm getting at. And in city apartments all it takes is the walk from the bathroom to the bedroom to get your feet all dirty again. Sandals beat bedroom slippers because they're easier to get into and they don't get all gunky inside after you wear them for a while. (Did you know that dirty feet are more apt to hurt than clean ones? And that you're more apt to get blisters wearing dirty stockings than if your stockings are clean?) Get your thongs at the five-and-dime for 59¢.

◆ BLACK BALLET SLIPPERS

The ones ballerinas wear at rehearsals. They take the place of bedroom slippers for sitting around the apartment, and they're fine to wear with slacks, entertaining at home. (And after Chapter Eight, you just may be doing ballet exercises every morning.)

◆ RUBBERS

Go ahead, get some. I know they're ugly, but they have a purpose. Every once in a while it rains in the summertime, though I know it's not supposed to. And who wants to wear boots in the summer? Yet who wants to pay the thirty dollars for a new pair of shoes?

◆ BOOTS

It's the same thing as with raincoats. The prettier they are, the uglier. Boots are boots. They're here because otherwise your feet get wet. It's appalling how many women fell for those tootsy "Puss 'n Boots" boots when the boot craze first hit. Some even went to the theater with sequins and slop all over their little cloth boots (that, by the way, leak).

Get some black rubber boots that look like the ones firemen wear (they're cheap). Wear them to the fanciest of balls, the grubbiest of dogfights. Wear them all winter long. Your feet will stay dry and you will stay chic, I promise.

◆ HANDBAGS

Two. One leather, one silk. Remember Geri's

words back there on shoes, "You're right if your leather is right"? Well, don't forget them. Handbags are another tell-everything. You should have one bag for day that will go with everything you own—spring, summer, fall, winter. It is your constant companion, with you almost every minute of the year. So don't associate with trash. Pay!

Nine years ago Adele splurged and spent four hundred dollars for a black alligator Hermes handbag. That was nine years ago. She's carried it every day since. Did she throw four hundred dollars away? I don't think she did. And from the looks of it, she'll be carrying it for another nine years. I'm not saying go out and spend four hundred on a handbag. Good God, that's more money than most of us see in a month. But I'm saying not to spend eighteen on one you're only half proud of "to last until you can afford a good one." Life is too short.

Sixty dollars is a good price. Sixty dollars for two years (that's 730 days) is a very good price.

The silk bag for evening isn't so important. I'm not even against those three-dollar silk envelopes you see around everywhere. Certainly don't go spending good money on an Italian beaded bag. If you have that kind of money, spend it on the leather one.

◆ SCARVES
Nine. Again, play. Do whatever you want with scarves. You can get any color you want—even mint green. Plaids, polka dots, abstracts, solids,

whatever pleases you. Don't get them at the five-and-dime, however, because they're always sleazy and too sheer. But they needn't be wildly expensive, either. I like the fifty-cent farmer's handkerchief in bright red from the Army-Navy store. In other words, better cotton than cheap synthetic.

◈ GLOVES

Two pair. Did you know that there's been an absolute thing about gloves in the past few years? There has. A glove now isn't a glove unless it's leather. Cotton gloves are only for tourists, and that's not a compliment.

Get one pair of twelve-button white kid gloves. Twelve-button means to the elbow. It used to be that you couldn't go through a receiving line without wearing those awful full-length gloves, right up under the armpit like the ones brides and debutantes wear. You used to have to arrive at the dance wearing them, and then if you had anything to eat, drink, or smoke, you'd unbutton them at the wrist and tuck them up under inside, so it looked as if you had two large tumors on the bottom parts of your wrists. You used to *have* to do that. It was *de rigeur*, that's all. As standard as saying "How do you do?" when you're introduced. You were unknowing if you arrived gloveless. It was like replying, "Pleased ta meecha." But then again, time used to be when all "ladies" wore hats too.

Thank God, times change. Now you don't

have to wear gloves at all. I didn't even wear them at my wedding, and my wedding was a formal one. If they're elbow-length, no one will notice. You'll just carry them, anyway. And these twelve-button gloves can go to cocktail parties too.

The next pair should be eight-button length and black. Kid. Eight-button means halfway between the elbow and the wrist. Bear in mind the sleeves of your coat. If they are shorter than this, buy longer gloves. Because skin between the glove and coat sleeve is ugly. And cold.

Gloves that are lined are bulky. But some women have poor circulation in the winter and need the extra warmth. Don't wear fur-lined gloves in the city.

◆ MITTENS
One pair. Heavy and warm. You may be asked to the country. Snowball fights.

◆ BIG MAN'S WATCH
One. Most girls get good watches for graduation, but I didn't. If you did, good watch for you. But I didn't. Well, for years I tried to save the money myself to buy a good watch because I never knew what time it was. Finally, in desperation, I bought a big hunky man's watch on sale at a department store for $4.99 with a one-year guarantee. And then I wore it.

You know, it's marvelous. Watches, like boots, I have since decided, are functional. Maybe I've decided that because I love to rationalize and because I have a large ego. Perhaps. But now I think jewelry designers have just been fooling us with the tricky, pretty watches. They've made them look like bracelets, with little things that clamp over the faces, all studded with color and craft. Or they've made the fancy little watch rings. Or the little hanging pins that you're supposed to stick on the outermost part of your boobie so you don't have to strain your neck to see. Or they've made tiny little watch-watches that are *so* tiny you have to take out your glasses in order to read what they say. *I* say, phooey. Get a big hunky man's watch for five dollars with a one-year guarantee, and know what time of day it is. Lots of the girls are wearing them now. (Make sure it's gold. Not real gold—just gold.)

◈ EXPENSIVE SUNGLASSES
One. Big ones. Men's. No white frames. (What man do you know who would wear white frames?) No rhinestones. (What man do you know who would wear rhinestones?) No different-colored detachable doodads that clip on, every day a different clip-on, to match whatever it is you're wearing. *No!*

◈ UMBRELLA
One. You'll lose it, I know it; why fight it?— that's that. Still, no excuse to carry around shiny rayon and plastic handles. Get a good umbrella.

A silk umbrella with a wooden handle. Cut off the wrist loops and carry it by the shaft. (Wrist loops are rather like belt loops, in my book.)

Don't buy a "happy singing in the rain" umbrella with flowers and things. They're like boots and raincoats and television sets, umbrellas. The prettier, the uglier.

◈ PERFUME

Yes, wear perfume or at least cologne. A lot of the girls in New York are wearing men's cologne now because it smells so clean, not sweet, and it's not expensive. Only wear one scent. In other words, buy deodorant to match your cologne. A lot of different smells at once is confusing and can be offensive.

◈ JEWELRY IN GENERAL

Forget it. Spend your money elsewhere. Audrey Hepburn makes a million dollars a movie and she doesn't wear jewelry, so you don't have to, either. If you have some baubles already, that's one thing. But don't buy them yourself.

◈ TRADEMARKS

Three. What's a trademark? It's something that's *yours*. It can be almost anything. A funny pin your grandmother left you when she died, or a belt with a strange buckle. Earrings can be great trademarks, especially if you have pierced ears. So can rings. It can even be a perfume, so long as you've worn only that brand, for, say, two years. You should wear at least two of your three trademarks every day.

Trademarks, by the way, are inevitably picked up by other women. Don't be sorry—imitation is the highest form of flattery.

4

n Skin

◆ I have this friend Marra, who—in spite of her very fine figure, her warm personality, her zest for living, her good taste in clothes, her quick wit and intelligence—had a repellent quality about her.

She never looked clean. In fact, she looked as though she smelled. I never actually went up and had a sniff, but even if she didn't have halitosis, she should have. You know? Her clothes were clean, but I imagined they smelled under the arms. There was some little something that said "Stay away" about her; but I never figured out just what it was until she had gotten rid of the problem.

It was blackheads. How's that? Just good old ugly blackheads.

Now she looks clean. And can you think of any one thing more attractive than cleanliness? I've been thinking and I can't. Cleanliness is not only next to godliness, it's magnetic. And it's sexy.

And good skin is the most obvious indication of cleanliness there is. Let's face it—if you can't take care of a shiny nose, how are you going to convince your audience you wash out your underwear at night? Lift up your skirt?

If you have a real skin problem—acne, for example—a dermatologist is the only answer. There are so many causes of acne that there have to be that many different treatments. A doctor will treat *your* skin, not skin in general. So I am speaking only of so-called "normal" skin.

◆ Good skin is habit—that's what good skin is. "Nothing works now and then," as Sunny Harnett would say. (Sunny Harnett, for twelve years a top model, now handles the "new girls" at Ford's Model Agency in New York.)

You can use anything. I know a girl who uses baby oil. But she uses it every single night, even when she doesn't feel like it. It's so easy to get home from a date too late, and a little tipsy besides, and just plop down on the bed and say, "One night won't matter." But it does. Not only do you wake up the next morning feeling really rotten, but if you can do that one night, then you can do it another night. And another. It's like the little man and his dishes. You know the story. He was too tired to wash them one night,

48

and the next night he was *twice* as tired, and so on until he was eating out of the soap dish. You get the point. EVERY night.

Here's what you do every night:

◆ Lift the hair off your face and neck with a headband or shower cap.

◆ Take baby oil (mascara remover if you're rich, but it's all the same) and slobber generously on first one eyelid and then the other. Take a tissue and pull gently on the upper lashes to remove the coating of mascara. (It may take another slobbering of oil.) Then remove the eye liner. Last, gently pull on the lower lashes to get rid of the mascara there, and follow it up by rubbing an oil-saturated Q-Tip along the lower part of the eye between the skin and the lashes. (This not only removes any black smudge, but it's good for that area of the face that ages the quickest.)

◆ Glob cold cream all over your face. Rub it in, then wipe it off with a clean tissue. Smear on a second helping. Tissue *it* off.

◆ Suds your face with special facial soap. Rub circularly in an upward direction (it's good for the circulation and wrinkle prevention) until your face feels so clean it sings.

◆ Take a clean (every day a clean one) washcloth, and fill it with hot water. Close your eyes.

Splash the water all over your face and hold the washcloth there to steam out your blackheads.

◈ Rub the special soap into the washcloth and scrub your neck and ears. Rinse off.

◈ Splash very cold water on your face.

◈ Take a cotton ball and saturate it with witch hazel or a mild astringent (never alcohol—it's too harsh) and wipe gently around the "oil areas"—the nose and chin. Look at the cotton ball. Is there a trace of dirt on it? There shouldn't be. And next morning is there a trace of black smudge on your pillow? There shouldn't be.

Do that every night and you've got a habit.

◈ Then every week, or as often as you wash your hair, give yourself a facial sauna. What you do is this: Bring a pot of water to a heavy boil, turn down the stove, and let it simmer for five minutes. Meanwhile remove all makeup and soil from your face. You know how to do that. Take the pot from the stove, put it on a low table, sit down with a towel thrown over your head and the pot (to keep the vapors in), and sit there as long as you think you can stand it. Fifteen minutes was it for me. The steam gets right into your skin and opens the pores and gets rid of the poisons. You'll begin to perspire like you've never perspired in your life.

When the fifteen minutes are up, go into the bathroom and start squeezing your blackheads.

(Cover your two index fingers with clean tissue and squeeze *gently*.) Only squeeze for about five minutes; you can tell when to stop because the pores will begin to close and you will find you have to squeeze harder. Remember: if it's hurting you, then stop. You are probably damaging your skin. Now scrub gently with your facial soap and clean facecloth. Rinse with icy-cold water—even ice water—and pat-dry with a rough towel. Saturate a cotton ball with mild astringent and pat onto the face. Then let the air dry it off. You won't believe how clean you feel.

If you knew what a blackhead was, you'd gag. What a blackhead is, is secreted oils that have accumulated and clogged at the hair follicle opening. (All those holes you call "pores" are hair follicle openings.) The black part of the blackhead is not, contrary to popular opinion, dirt. It is the result of a chemical reaction the dried-up oils have when they are exposed to air after a period of time. That's why mere washing, or scrubbing, will not get rid of the black. You have to get rid of the whole thing. All or nothing at all.

The oils become clogged at the follicle opening for many reasons. One is that the openings are not kept clean. Another is that the "horny" layer (that's what the man said) is producing cells faster than the cells are dying and shedding, so they cover the follicle openings and nothing can get out. That's why scrubbing with facial soap works so well—it helps remove that outer layer. So does sun. Sun in moderation, that is.

You've noticed how much better your skin seems in the summer, and I don't mean just color. It's because of that "horny" layer—the sun hastens the scaling-off process. Sun also causes the skin to manufacture vitamin D which promotes general good health, and general good health is good for the skin.

Too much sun (i.e., sunburn) is worse than none. Skin cancer aside (fear of lung cancer still hasn't gotten me to give up smoking), think of the wrinkles. Sunburn destroys the something-or-other fibers of the epidermis and they lose their elasticity.

By the way, if every summer you walk around with a beet-red nose, try removing your sunglasses when you're in the sun. The reflection off the glass part gives your nose maybe twice the amount of sun as the rest of you. Wear false eyelashes instead. At the beach, squint.

All vitamins are a help, as I mentioned before, because they promote general good health. But there are specific vitamins that directly affect your skin. Vitamin C, for example. Vitamin C not only helps you resist common colds; it also helps "healing." Drink a glass of grapefruit or orange juice a day. But do it every day, because the body cannot store vitamin C.

Vitamin A helps to slow down the production of these "horny layer" cells. And conversely it speeds up the dying and shedding process. So your oils won't get plugged—remember?

Take a multi-vitamin capsule every day with your orange juice and you needn't worry further.

Just watch what goes into your mouth. If it's a lot of gunk, then guaranteed, a lot of gunk is going to show up on your face. Butter is gunk, and so are sweets. You know what's gunk as well as I do.

Now get eight hours of sleep a night. You need it, I need it, everybody does. Sometimes you can get by with less, but you're the slightest bit more irritable the next day, and that's ultimately not good for your skin. Did you know that such things as irritation, worry and fear can upset the hormone cart and trigger an over-activity of those oil glands?

And hands off, for God's sake. Even resting your chin in your hands is going to push oil and perspiration and bacteria into the "follicle openings."

So that's skin. I haven't even discussed the big stuff like "pustules" and "cysts," and I don't intend to. I repeat—if you have what you'd call acne, then get on the phone this minute and make an appointment with a dermatologist. This minute.

5

n Hair

◈ When I first came to New York I thought the important thing was that evening, that day. Tomorrow we may die. If my hair was a mess, then I'd tease, rat, snarl, pull, yank, spray—anything to fix the immediate problem. Then a couple of years later I looked in the mirror and discovered that I didn't have hair any more; it was some sort of queer cross between hay and wire. *I* didn't even want to touch it. No one else did, either. I began to wear scarves to work more and more often. Finally I complained to a model-friend who turned me on to a genius named Don Lee. Now my hair is looking like hair again.

Healthy hair is beautiful hair. Healthy hair swings. To understand how to make hair healthy, it's first necessary to understand what hair actually is. Each strand of hair is made up of cuticles that lie on top of each other like scales lie on fish. When the hair is not damaged (there isn't really any such thing as "healthy" hair—hair is dead as soon as it gets outside of the follicle opening; what we see is always dead), the cuticles lie flat on the shaft, and thus the hair is shiny. When the hair is damaged, the cuticles tend to stick out—and a dry, dead-to-the-touch effect has to be the result.

Hair is most often damaged simply because the hair follicle is clogged for some reason and the natural oils produced inside the scalp are unable to reach the ends and those cuticles stick out. This is more common than one would think. Don Lee claims that a majority of men and women have at least a "low-key" scalp infection that causes this.

But most people are not aware of any scalp infection other than dandruff. Dandruff is another big misconception. Popular opinion has it that dandruff is the result of a dry scalp. And that dandruff is contagious. Well, not so. Each hair has at least one oil gland. Usually when there is overactivity of the oil glands in the skin (acne), it is accompanied by overactivity of the oil glands in the scalp as well. Layer after layer of oil settles on the scalp and stays there. These layers of excess oil make a marvelous nest for bacteria. Now there's no avoiding bacteria. It's cn your face, it's in your scalp, it's in the air, everywhere. It's nothing to get excited about. But when bacteria has a place to hang its hat—

those layers of oil—then worry. They will reproduce and spread at a fantastic speed.

The irritation from the excessive oil and the infection from the bacteria set up a mild inflammation in the cells of the scalp. They die and shed. The dead cells mixed with the dried-up oils form flaking and scaling. And that, my friends, spells dandruff. Not dry scalp. And it's not your kid sister's fault because she borrowed your brush once. It's your own overactive oil glands and your unclean scalp.

◆ Bad bleaching jobs and bad straightening jobs can also cause damage. (So can bad permanents, but who has permanents these days?) I don't believe in bleaching on principle—forget the damage. Nature usually matches complexions to suit hair color. So when you change your hair color you usually have to change your face color too. Which can be done, of course, with makeup. But then you're left with this mask that stops at the neck. And your body doesn't go with your head. What do you do on the beach? So I wouldn't bleach. Highlighting is a different story, but highlighting doesn't damage the hair.

I do believe in straightening even though it often causes damage. Remember how old Jackie Kennedy looked at her wedding and how young she looks today? It's straightening. Hair has to swing. I already said that. And only healthy hair can do that. Unhealthy hair just hangs. That's all true. But curly hair can't swing, either. Curly hair just kinks. Kinky, frizzy hair never looks healthy, even if it is.

So if you need to, have it straightened. The only problem is that you risk ruining your hair. And that is a problem. Have it done, but make sure it's an expert who is doing it. Don't, whatever you do, do it yourself. Straightening is not to be messed with at home. Straighteners are harsh at best. Some have lye in them. And lye is not a gentle thing.

I have extremely curly hair, but I only allow myself the luxury of a straightening job once a year. The winter is never much of a problem. So it frizzes if you don't set it. So you set it. Big deal. But the summer isn't so simple—humidity means frizz, set or no set. If you can possibly get through the April showers, then you can wait until the very end of May. And if you do that, you don't need to straighten it again until the following April showers. And if you can resist those again, you can wait for the end of May. And so on.

Once you've had it straightened, take extra good care with your hair. Brush every night at least a hundred strokes with a natural-bristles brush. If you don't understand why not to use nylon, then have a compare sometime under a magnifier. I did and I'll never use nylon again. The ends of the nylon bristles are as sharp as broken glass. Natural bristles are rounded at the ends. It's like the difference between rubber-tipped bobby pins versus the non-rubber-tipped ones. Brushing vigorously stimulates the circulation in the scalp and helps carry these oils from the scalp down to the ends of the hair shafts.

◈ Your shampoo should not be harsh. But most of them are. Most of the commercial shampoos on the market are detergents, which are less expensive to manufacture, but they are harsh. They take everything out of your hair. Some try to make up for it by putting other things back in, like lanolin and egg and all that stuff, but it's better never to take away what's already there. Castile soap is the softest, according to my friend Don Lee. Suds twice. The first time around just eliminates dirt and excess oils. The second sudsing does the cleaning. Remember that the point of shampooing is to clean the scalp, not the hair. Of course sometimes it's difficult to avoid the hair. Especially if it's short. But brushing cleans the hair. It's the scalp you're after.

While you're shampooing give yourself a head massage. Work the lather in vigorously. Squinch your scalp; it should be loose. Everyone who gets treated by Don Lee has the most glorious twenty-five-minute neck, shoulder, and head massage imaginable. Just plain old tension can make the scalp tight and thus cut down the circulation, so your scalp doesn't get fed properly, and ultimately one of those "low-key" scalp infections can occur. And you know what happens then—your natural oils don't ever reach the ends of your hair. Tension! Isn't that a riot? And

58

you don't have to be the executive vice-president of General Motors to suffer from that. I know a lot of tense receptionists.

Shampoo absolutely whenever you know you should. Everyone should shampoo at least once a week, but some need to every two or three days. If you fall into that category, don't shirk. You'll regret it.

Don't stop there. Cream rinse after every shampoo. You know that ad, "It's a shame to shampoo without Tame"? It *is* a shame. Cream rinses don't do any permanent good, but they coat the hair shafts and give a little protection until the next shampoo. And they tend to smooth down those scraggly cuticles. Conditioners like Flex, Clairol's Condition, and the Wella treatment work much the same way. I've found they don't do anything lasting for me, but the temporary good is good enough.

I use the conditioner once a week when I'm having my facial sauna. The hair absorbs more of the oil with heat, and there's plenty of that from all the steam. If you put a plastic bag over your hair, the oil doesn't drip down onto your face.

After shampooing, brunettes should rinse with a half-vinegar–half-water solution to cut the soap. The smallest amount of soap left on the hair makes for dull, boring hair. If you're a blonde, do the same thing with lemon juice. It works the same way, and you have the added attraction of bringing out your blond highlights.

◆ As long as we're in the kitchen, let's talk about some other of the wives' tales. Yes, beer and champagne give body to your hair and make fine setting lotions. They do no damage whatsoever. They're equally effective, but of course it's much spiffier to say you use champagne. Eggs and milk in your shampoos work like cream rinses. They're fine too.

If I sound hung up on health in all this, it's because I am. I tried it the other way, the fake way—the yanking, ratting, spraying way—and it didn't work. I always looked a mess. I have the feeling the reason our grandmothers and mothers went out and bought hats when they were depressed instead of having their hair done, like we do, is because their hair could never swing. It was never as healthy as ours is today. In those days you washed your hair once every two weeks if you needed to or not, and that was that. It was unhealthy to shampoo more often. Or so they thought. So they bought hats.

◆ Some of my friends don't know how to set their own hair. It's amazing. How can anyone not know how to take care of their own hair? I was washing and setting mine at the age of seven. Sure, I go to the hairdresser every so often —always when it needs a cut or trim—but a stupid old wash and set? I can do it myself, thanks.

It's so limiting not to know how to care for your hair. What if you go swimming on a Sunday and have a heavy date Sunday night? The beauty shops are closed on Sundays. And financially it's staggering. You figure it's close to $10 a week what with tipping, taxis to and from, etc. That's $520 a year before you've even had a haircut!

So if it's the initial expense involved that's keeping you from doing your own, don't be naïve. Hair dryers cost anywhere from $25 to $125. But whatever you pay, it pays for itself within a couple of months. If you have straight hair, you may want to get a curling iron ($5 to $10) or the Carmen curler kit ($50). If, on the other hand, you've been cursed with curls, a good electric comb will cost you from $35 to $45. But I bought a stand-up hair dryer a couple of years ago for sixty dollars. My husband thought I was being ridiculously extravagant. Well, the way I figure it, that sixty dollars has saved me close to a thousand.

Stand-up dryers are the fastest, of course. But those portable ones with the big soft caps aren't bad, either. And, as I say, they're portable. And infinitely less expensive. The hair dryer I would *not* buy is that air-conditioner dryer that looks so professional and sits on a table top. You know, it's got that hard football helmet just like the stand-up jobs. Awfully impressive. The problem is it takes forever to dry strand number one. I finally gave mine to the girl upstairs. Let her sit there all night getting kinks in her neck. Better she than me.

Now I'm not even tempted to have my hair done. It takes too long. If there's one thing I can't bear doing much of, it's waiting around. And all I do at the hairdresser's is just that. Wait to get washed, wait to get set, wait for a free dryer, wait to get out of it, wait to get combed through once I am out, then wait around to pay the check. It's three and a half hours no matter what he promises. I love him dearly, he's a genius, but who has three and a half hours? So now I go only when I need a cut or trim.

You must have a hair dryer if you're going to do your own hair. Sleeping on rollers is the worst. Clips cut the hairs when you toss and turn, and the tension of that pulling on the scalp for eight hours is damaging indeed. Some don't believe in dryers because they think heat dehydrates hair. Of course it dehydrates hair. That's the point. But after the hair is dry it picks up whatever moisture there is in the air, just like skin does after a sauna bath.

If you have straight hair, I'm jealous. All you have to do is blow your hair dry with one of those hand-held dryers and next morning take five minutes to Carmen-curl it. The Carmen curl kit is the size of a small shoe box and contains approximately twenty rollers. They sit on electrically heated prongs, which heat the rollers, which in turn curl your hair. It all happens like that. You start putting the heated rollers in your hair, and by the time you're through you start taking them out. Like that. Put in, take out. Punkt. You're gorgeous. For $50. (Q.H.S. also makes you gorgeous for more fuss and much less money.)

Curling irons are another poor man's Carmen curler. They're infinitely more difficult to master the art of, and if you haven't mastered the art, you risk burning your hair off. But they're cheap.

There are two kinds of electric combs—the good ones and the rotten ones. The rotten ones cost $5 or so, and they don't do anything much except burn your hair. The good ones blow hot air out while they comb. You can buy these only at wholesale beauty-supply places, and still they cost you something in the neighborhood of $35. They're great to bring with you on weekends by the seashore—you can return from the beach all kinked up and get straightened out in no time. Have your hairdresser teach you how to use them.

But at Vidal Sassoon, where they believe in straight hair as much as I do, they use plain old hand-held dryers with brushes instead of the electric combs. You pull a section of hair tight by wrapping it around the brush part of the brush, aim the hot air from the dryer at this arrangement, then pull gently on the brush until the kink is gone. It works.

The rest is chicken feed: fifteen mesh rollers the diameter of silver dollars and ten the size of quarters, a giant-size triangular net that will fit over all that mess and keep it in place, huge and heavy hairpins instead of clips, rubber-tipped bobby pins if you can't work the hairpins, setting lotion, a dog brush, a big hardy natural-bristles brush for your bureau, a small natural-bristles brush for your purse, a large sturdy comb (*not* a teasing comb), scotch tape if your hair is short, a Kotex or large wad of cotton if you have bangs, Coets so your ears don't burn under the dryer, end papers if you can handle them, hair spray, and some dry shampoo in case He calls the night you were going to wash your hair. Your hair wardrobe is complete.

The mesh rollers with the metal rims are the best if you can learn to use the heavy hairpins instead of the clips. (You can't stick hairpins through solid rollers.) And the reasons for using hairpins are many. First off, they don't dent your hairdo as clips are apt to; they don't pull the hair and cause unnecessary breakage, and they don't burn your scalp under the dryer because they never touch it. I can't give you directions on how to use them—you just have to play with them awhile. Basically all you do is roll the hair around the mesh roller and stick the heavy hairpin right through the center. If you just can't handle the hairpins, use rubber-tipped bobby pins. They don't cause breakage, and they make for more tension, thus a better set.

Beer or setting lotions give the hair more superficial body—body is simply a matter of fluids getting down into the hair. (But if your fluids aren't working properly, it's better to have artificial body than no body at all. Otherwise the temptation is to rat, tease, and snarl.) Some setting lotions are bad for the hair, however. They contain chemicals that absorb the moisture in the

air and don't allow any to get to the hair itself.
I've found that protein lotions, like Kindness,
Pantene, and Renee, cause no dehydration, but
of course they cost. Beer's cheap, and it works
just as well after it has gone dead.

◆ You should have three brushes. A dog brush
(that's right, a dog brush—with wire, not hair)
is a must if you have a hair piece. But even if
you haven't, they are great for getting rid of
tangles—just take care not to pull too hard. And
don't go rubbing your scalp with a dog brush.
The brush for doing your hundred strokes a
night should have sturdy, hardy natural bristles.
They should be tough enough to get right
through the hair to increase scalp circulation.
And carry a small natural-bristles brush in your
purse. It's always better to brush than comb.

If you have to tease, and everyone has to a
little, tease with a large comb with teeth that are
relatively wide apart. Don't tease with a brush—
that causes the cuticles to stick out. *And don't
use a teasing comb!* When the hair is wet, it
snarls more readily; a large-toothed comb gets
through the hair easier when you're setting after
shampoos.

If you have very short hair, you'll probably
set only the crown of your head in rollers. Set
the bottom by placing scotch tape over it. Scotch
tape keeps side bangs straight too. But if your
bangs go across the entire forehead, comb them
in sections over a Kotex or a large wad of cotton.

Dry shampoo (or plain old powder) is a wonderful hair first aid if the imminent shampoo is impossible and the hair has gone a little greasy. It is not in any way damaging to your scalp or hair.

Hair spray, of course, is. In fact, hair spray is the worst destroyer of healthy hair. But use it you shall, as I shall. Just use it wisely. (Wisely is as little as possible.) Spray it on your brush, not directly on your hair. Don't let it get at the scalp.

◆ The only thing I'm going to say about hair styles is that I don't think you should get too hung up on what hairdo is appropriate to the shape of your head. I know girls who try to fix their Valentine-shaped faces or their pear-shaped faces, and, oh yes, the shapes of their heads come out oval in the end, but they walk around with oval heads and 1942 hairdos. My belief is that if you happened to be born with a pear-shaped face, don't worry about it. Pear-shaped heads can be charming. So can Valentines.

Most of today's hairdos have nothing whatsoever to do with the shape of your head; they have to do with the shape of your hair. If it's healthy, if it swings, it's flattering whatever the shape of your head.

Hair is ideally either very long or extraordinarily short these days. But there are lots of middle-of-the-roaders like me who are in the process of getting very long hair. Even the

66

middle of the road can be attractive if the hair is healthy.

The cut is as important to hair as it is to clothes. No matter how beautiful the fabric, if the cut of the dress is ugly, the dress has got to be ugly. The same is true with hair. Paul McGregor, one of New York's most with-it hairdressers, says the proof of the pudding is the way it grows out. A good cut grows out gracefully. A bad one looks like the in-between stage within six weeks.

Cut is infinitely more important than the set. You can't turn a bad cut into a good hairdo no matter which way you put the rollers in—but you can hardly muck up a good cut, however you set it.

The mistake so many girls make is going into the hairdresser when they're a little down and out, saying, "Do whatever you want to do." Well, what if your hairdresser's down and out that day too? You may feel like a change, but remember a total change sometimes takes a long time to grow out.

One last word about styles. Any daytime style that looks "done," that shows clearly that you've just come from the hairdresser, is unfeminine in my book. My idea of women who wear perfect little "coifed coifs" is that they wear tight girdles too. That they probably organize their husbands the way they organize their weekly menus. The whole point of hair is that it's terribly sexy—let's admit that immediately. And what man wants to run his fingers through a lot of spray and perfection?

◈ Now let's get to the most expensive item in this book—the hair piece, or the "fall." Until a year ago, when I got my first hair piece, I would have put them in the gravy category. But now that I have one I don't see how I ever got along before. I wear it all the time.

Hair pieces certainly beat dry shampoo for emergencies. And even when your hair is clean and set, a hair piece adds thickness so you don't have to tease the health out of your own. And if you have short hair, but sometimes get the urge to wear it long, well, then you can.

The trouble with hair pieces is they cost you. You're going to have to pay at least $100 for a good fall of human hair, and it won't be a very long fall at that. The longer they are, the more expensive; they go up to $800.

It's difficult to know whether you're going to get a good one or a bad one when you walk in to buy one. The only thing to do is to go to a reliable salon that will stand behind their hair. Frizzy, kinky hair can be set to look straight and great, but once you're out in the humid Hamptons, it will start kinking and frizzing.

Hair pieces come on many different-shaped and -sized bases. Sometimes the hair is attached right to a headband. (I don't think they're very practical, though, because it limits you to always wearing a headband.) The ones with only bases are very easy to attach. What you do is you take enough hair from the top of your head to fill two rollers and drop that forward, over your eyes. Then you make two pin curls with bobby pins immediately behind that clump of hair that's in your eyes. Then just stick the comb on the hair piece under the pin curls. (If your hair piece hasn't a comb, do the same thing with those long heavy hairpins.) Tease and smooth the clump—it's really annoying you by now—over the top of all of this, and no one will ever know it's not yours.

6

n Makeup

◆ My ex-roommate and I went to a cocktail party a few years ago. And I can still remember that little turquoisc-eyelidded wonder who came up to her with, "Boy, I wish I could look as well as you do without any makeup."

I stifled my guffaw while Linda feigned a proper blush and said only, "Why, thank you!"

No makeup, indeed. I knew different. I was there—yelling at her through the door of the bathroom while she stood at the mirror, her drugstore spread out on the sink. Glueing the eyelashes on. Painting the lines over the lids. The powder. The rouge. The eye shadow, the eyebrow pencil. The whole bit—you name it, she

70

had it on. "Come on!" I kept screaming. "The party will be over before we get there."

But when that poor painted doll looked at her with envy in her eyes, I had to admit that Linda seemed as if all she were wearing was the fresh blush of youth. *That's the Secret!*

Why bother if you just want to look natural? Is that what you're saying? That's what I used to say too. "Makeup is just bad for your skin, anyway." Then I came to New York and saw things differently. I met a model named Iris Bianchi who has been modeling since she was seventeen, and she's still going strong. I'm not sure of her age, but she has a ten-year-old daughter, so that should give you a hint. Her skin is wrinkleless, blemishless, flawless. She's been wearing makeup since she was seventeen, and if my skin looked like hers even now, I'd consider myself a beauty. Makeup by itself is not damaging to your skin—so long as you keep it clean. Of course if you wear makeup and don't get it all off at night . . . It's like food and your teeth. Food causes decay if you don't brush it out, but that doesn't mean it's bad for your teeth.

Now, why bother to wear makeup at all? Linda looked "natural" without any makeup, but she was lacking that fresh blush of youth. Her skin, by itself, was a bit pasty and porous. She had a "natural" redness around her nose and "natural" dark circles under her eyes. And her eyelashes were naturally sparse and stubby. That's why you should wear makeup.

71

◆ I was lucky. Soon after my decision to try makeup my aunt took me for a two-month trip around the world. Aside from the obvious cultural benefits, it was a great opportunity for me to learn about my face. No one had any preconceived ideas of what I should look like—so every day I had the opportunity to look completely different.

At first, different was silly. But by the time we reached Honolulu (we began in Rome), I was well on the way to having a look of my own.

In Rome I set my hair one way, in Athens, another. In Cairo I tried a different shape to my eyebrows, in Jerusalem, a different eye liner. And so on, through India, Burma, Thailand, Japan. In other words, I had the time and the freedom—the freedom of not being around people who expected me to look a certain way—to experiment. And experiment I did.

I'd cover my face with pancake makeup, even the eyebrows, and look in the mirror with a light shining directly from the side. I'd see where my eyes ended and my nose began as a sculptor would see. I'd see my big chin with its ridiculous dimple and my short, fat nose. The things I couldn't change. So I didn't try to change them.

Then I would take the light back with me about six feet from the mirror and apply the eyebrow pencil. Sometimes I'd do it straight across, sometimes with an arch. Sometimes turning the ends up, sometimes down. And so on, as I say, through the Mid and Far East, all the way to San Francisco and New York.

What those sixty days taught me is as simple as this: DON'T FIGHT NATURE, HELP IT.

The eyebrows are a good example. Don't fight them. Help them. If they are naturally arched, leave them alone. If they run straight across, Cleopatra-style, fine for you. Whatever they are they are and should be.

I also learned that applying makeup is a whole routine and has to be treated as such. Do it step by step. Taking one step before the previous steps have been taken can prove disastrous. Like putting on the mascara before you put on your foundation. Fortunately the process is 90 per cent common sense.

Here's the full routine, from the beginning:

◆ Begin with a spanking clean face. You can't get that fresh-blush-of-youth effect if you're just adding to yesterday's.

◆ If you need it, use a little moisturizer.

◆ Foundation is next. It should be exactly the color of your skin minus the pink. If it's darker, it's going to show at the neck, and if you have to extend it way down to the collar, your collar's going to get dirty. What do you do when you wear a low-cut dress? Don't cheat on this. The exact same color.

It can be liquid or cake or cream, whatever you like. Some people get immune and have to switch foundations every couple of months, like deodorants. It has to do with your chemistry.

73

Pat the makeup onto your face, don't rub. Pat it all over, evenly. The function of makeup is not to hide blemishes (it can never do that); it's to even things out. Like the redness around your nose. It makes the forehead the same color as your chin. In a way, you're just preparing your canvas. After the foundation is on the fun begins.

◈ Use a tissue if your foundation has an oil base. I use "Fresh-Ups," which are just tiny pieces of chemically treated tissues that absorb the oils but don't affect the makeup. I like a relatively shiny look (not to be confused with an oily look), so I hardly ever put on powder right after I apply foundation. It's a good idea to use "Fresh-Ups" even if you use powder, so the powder won't glop together. Press—don't rub.

◈ If you do wear powder, wear it loose and translucent. (To quote another model friend, "Translucent powder makes all other powders seem like chalk dust.") Use a big puff and fluff on a generous amount all over the face. Then fluff off the excess. It leaves you with a soft matte "finished" finish. Use the pressed translucent powder for touching up. (Clean puff every day!) And pat it on firmly—don't rub.

◈ The beauty editor of *Glamour* magazine said recently, "I don't know any girl who couldn't improve her looks with eye liner." I agree with her. But eye liner used badly is far worse than none. The thing you must do is really look at the shape of your eyes and decide what shape is for you. My eyes are smaller than I'd like them to be, so I use the liner to make them look rounder. Whatever shape you decide on, don't decide on those Barbra Streisand "flags" that stick out to the ears. Barbra Streisand can wear them because she's Barbra Streisand. But you aren't.

Don't use pencil, if only for the long-run reason—it pulls on your eyes and you'll get wrinkles there quicker. The liquid liner dries up within a couple of months. The tiny little cakes, however, last and last. Practice putting it on looking straight ahead without pulling the lid to the side—you have more control of the shape that way.

Don't use black—it's too harsh even if your hair is black. Get brown or gray. And don't get turquoise, or midnight blue or purple! You want to look like you, not Marcel Marceau.

◆ Eyebrow pencil is pretty nearly unnecessary if you have nicely shaped eyebrows, unless you're terribly blond. Even then I wouldn't bother. What used to be done with eyebrows is done now with eye shadow. If you've plucked them too much, however, and they look mangy or something, use it. But use it carefully.

Eyebrows, naturally, are tiny little hairs—not two heavy lines penciled on with a heavy hand. So when you pencil on eyebrows you should make them look like the little hairs that are supposed to be there. A big clumsy eyebrow pencil point isn't going to get anything near a hairlike result. Neither will that silly brush-on eyebrow stuff. Use the thin eye-liner pencil for your eyebrows. And nick off the tip every time you use it so you have a nice sharp edge.

Not black, even if your eyebrows are. Use charcoal gray or brown. I know a gorgeous blonde who uses just a No. 2 lead pencil.

◆ The eyelashes come next. First powder them with pressed powder, both the uppers and lowers. And then mascara. I prefer cake mascara to anything else—it's thicker. But as long as you powder first, any mascara will do the job.

Use black or dark-brown mascara even if you're a blonde.

If you decide to wear false eyelashes, don't end up looking false. They come off theatrical if you try for added length; be satisfied with the additional thickness.

Some eyelashes come pre-trimmed. But I find for everyday wear that none of them are pre-trimmed enough. And inevitably the strip is too long unless you stick the lash right into the corner of your eye, which can be very painful. So get yourself an X-Acto pen (it's a metal pen with a razor edge), find a block of wood somewhere, stick the lash down on the wood, and start cutting. Each hair should be a different length than the one next to it. Just like your own.

Applying false eyelashes is never simple, especially new lashes. After a while they sort of get used to your eyes, or you to the lashes, like comfortable shoes. But in the beginning they're a pain. Patience.

Before you actually apply the lashes you first must curl them. Either stick them into one of those eyelash curlers, or simply place the lashes on the index finger—one at a time, that is—and dig in with your thumbnail. Or you can wrap them in paper around a pencil overnight.

Then you must mold them around into a soft halfmoon shape, to go wth your eyelid.

All this has to be done before you put glue on, because from then on it's a study in mind over nerves. Forget false lashes if you have a hang-over—they'll wind up in your eyeball. Or you'll get glue smeared all over your eyelid. You must have your morning coffee before the glue goes on—hands are not allowed to shake.

So the lashes are curled and shaped, and you've had your cup of coffee. Now you put a small rim of that awful-smelling glue on the very edge of the lash—not onto the actual hair part. Blow on it for about five seconds. Hold on in the center of the lash with those twizzor things (half tweezers, half scissors), open your eyes, look straight ahead, and put the lash onto the lid—as close as possible to your own lash hairs. Immediately take a clean toothpick (not one you've used before that may have left-over glue on—a clean one) and poke *carefully* so the outsides of the false lash are where they belong. Where they belong is on the little ledge (everyone has one) between where the eyelashes end and the eyelid begins.

Once the edges of the false lash are where they belong, pinch your own lashes with the false ones all across the perimeter—so at every point both real and fake are touching. There, you've done it.

◆ If you're the sensitive type with pink around the edges of your eyes, I may have a trick. The only skin around the eye that's still naked to the public is that part of the lower lid that's between the eye itself and the beginning of the lower lashes. This "lower ledge," as we will call it, is the first place where redness shows up.

The trick is white eye liner. It's a ticklish business putting the white liner there because it tickles! You need to use a special brush, too, that you don't use for applying anything else—otherwise your lower ledge might end up brown, and brown is worse than red. Experiment. It's fabulous at night especially—like built-in "sparkle."

Some people put brown there on purpose! I hope you don't. It just makes your eyes look smaller. Don't draw a line under the lower lashes, either.

◆ We're almost through. Next step is shading rouge. Don't use the commercial ones you can buy everywhere, because all of them are too pink. Shading rouge should be so dark it's almost brown. It doesn't look brown on the skin—don't panic—it just looks great. Instant cheekbones. Eileen Ford, head of the model agency, has a good shading rouge you can get at Altman's, but last time I checked, you could get the same shade cheaper at the Make-Up Center on West 55th Street. If I didn't live in New York, I'd probably go to the drugstore and ask for Dorin's "Rouge Brunette—1249" (it's what the little old ladies have been wearing for years). Brush it on, though. Don't use the little puff that comes with it or you'll look like a little old lady.

Suck your cheeks in as if you're pulling on a thick milkshake through a straw. Look in the mirror. That should tell you where to brush it, in case you had a question.

◆ The final touch, of course, is lip gloss. Notice I say "gloss," not "stick." Pay attention. Not lipstick!

Lipstick ruins so many otherwise pretty faces. I see hundreds of them every day. Lipstick makes fifteen-year-olds look forty. It's harsh, blatant. It smacks you in the face. Lips. All lips, no eyes. Mouth. Pow. Big blabby mouth. If I were a man, I tell you, I'd never kiss a girl with that bright red gook on.

If you think you'd look like death without it, here's a little clue. Lipstick does not add color to your face. It merely draws attention to the fact that you haven't any anywhere else. What about that shading rouge? Get a sun lamp (don't fall asleep).

Have you ever noticed that ugly men are never quite so ugly as ugly women? It's because of lipstick, I'm convinced. Nature may have overlooked certain men, but at least they don't add to the trouble. (If they do, they're put in jail!)

The first thing I want to see when I look at a contemporary face is the eyes. But if you're wearing lipstick, all I see is red!

That's the routine. With lashes, count on twenty-five minutes; it should take about fifteen without them. Don't cheat on the time. You'll just cheat yourself.

I want to mention nail polish here, though it's not strictly "makeup," and it's certainly not part of this fifteen-minute routine.

Bright red nail polish is as old-hat as bright red lipstick. But if you don't wear any polish, your nails chip and break—right? And long nails make your fingers look longer, and so you want to let them grow. The clear polishes don't seem to protect them either. The frosted polishes are the answer at the moment. The polish should be on thick enough so you can't see through to the peeling layers beneath. This takes three coats. Let each coat dry before you apply the next. Gives you something to do under the hair dryer.

7

On Diet

◈ After reading the subway poster "Do blondes have more fun?" Judy went running down to her favorite beauty salon and had her hair done yellow. Judy spends three nights a week—and I mean from right after dinner to bedtime—doing those little girly things like plucking her eyebrows, polishing her nails, shampooing her hair, creaming her face.

But Judy is wasting her time. Judy's fat. And no matter how marvelous her eyes, how blond her hair, how pretty her feet, Judy remains fat.

There are too many Judys today who fuss with the specifics and ignore the whole. But, really, nothing matters if you're fat. The dress you wear doesn't make any difference. No one will notice whether your lipstick is pink or green. If your hemline sags, well, so do you. It's a sad truth, but pleasingly plump just isn't very pleasant.

And it's not modern. Look at the art of today. No more the fat Rubens nudes. They were fine then, when everyone sat around and drank wine. But today it's the shapeless, tall, skinny-like-an-arrow figures of Giacometti. Skin and bone and not much else. People today don't even *want* to sit back, drink wine, and be pampered. Even aristocrats (are there any left?) are getting out of their plush Louis XV chairs and getting involved in the world. It's an age of energy. And energy doesn't come from lugging around fifteen extra pounds.

Fat is a lethargic, lonely, scared-rabbit frame of mind. But fatties won't admit that. No, fatties are "jolly." Fatties won't admit that they eat too much. They'd sooner take a no-hope attitude and blame everything on their glands. Most fatties won't even admit that they're fat. (If I sound vehement, I am. Because I've been both places. I've been fat and I've been thin. And I could talk two weeks about the difference.)

But before you diet, figure out why it is you have to: you eat because you're empty inside, right? When empty means hungry, that's one thing. But when empty is empty—it's another thing again . . .

So the first step to dieting is to forget dieting for a while and concentrate on you. Do you have a project? Get one. Teach yourself Spanish.

82

Give yourself a six-week deadline to read the ten books you've been meaning to read for the past year. Collect stamps—I don't care. *Some*thing. Let it consume you. So you can't wait to get home from the office and get to work. (So you don't mind when the phone doesn't ring once you get there.) Get happy. *Then* you diet, when you have something else to think about besides food!

HOW NOT TO DIET

◆ Don't eat "because it's there." A working girl tends to get asked out often. The trouble is it's so sporadic. There may be five nights straight when she's invited for dinner, and then, conceivably, two weeks without so much as a movie. She never knows where her next free meal is coming from. So the temptation is to grab while the grabbing's good. Unfortunately these dinners happen more often than counted on. What on a Monday looks like an empty social week ahead may have proven crammed by Friday. And if you're the kind who gets taken for lunches *too*—well, my point is don't grab. Anyway, it's not becoming. You needn't give up the dinners—just don't order the specialty of the house if it's too rich and luscious. Like if you find yourself in an Italian restaurant, you can always order veal.

◆ And don't "diet tomorrow," which means feast today, preparing for tomorrow's famine.

(Tomorrow always turns into another today, with today's same annoyances and temptations.)

◈ Don't count calories. You'll probably only cheat, anyway.

◈ Don't eat those sugar-free substitutes. (Do, if you want to; I'll just tell you why I don't. Because the first thing I know, I'm eating "low-calorie" candy. And the "thinning kind of ice cream." Well, ice cream just isn't thinning.)

◈ Don't eat huge breakfasts and starve the rest of the day. Because you won't. When I eat a big breakfast I eat a bigger lunch. And by dinner I eat like a horse. On the other hand, when I begin the day with little or nothing, my appetite practically withers away.

◈ And don't diet for anyone else but you. Don't think that a gorgeous figure is going to bring your lost lover back or get you someone else's. Don't do it because you think it's going to solve your problems. When it turns out you still have problems—and you will (they're just nicer problems; they're the same problems minus ten pounds)—you'll just gain all your weight back by drowning your sorrow in pie. Diet because you want to. Because you'd like to feel the fun of really walking, not flapping, down the street. Because you'd like to wake up in the morning and stretch your muscles, not roll your rolls. You'd like to feel that your clothes are falling from your shoulders, not from the bulge in your back.

◆ And while you're dieting, *shut up about it!* No one cares.

HOW TO DIET
On the eve of his near-sixtieth birthday, Cary Grant said to the world, "Think thin." And the world laughed. But did it laugh wisely? I'm not so sure. I once talked myself out of twenty-five pounds in two months by thinking thin (and by thinking of Cary Grant). By asking myself, "Do I really want this slice of bread, this piece of pie?" And by realizing that I really didn't at all. "I'll have an apple instead." This whole diet business is in the mind.

Start by writing down on a list (a shopping list) all the "thinning" foods you would like to eat right now, this minute. Like luscious lettuce, huge thick steaks, and creamy cottage cheese. The list will get mammoth if you have any kind of imagination. Marvelous melons, crispy carrots. Cold consommé. Yummy yogurt. Peachy peaches. Gorgeous grapefruit. (By the way, there's a big thing about grapefruit in New York now. I see more and more people ordering it for dessert instead of an appetizer. When you finish a meal, finish it with a grapefruit. It makes you feel clean inside. It's fantastic—it really is. I have grapefruit every morning with coffee and exercises. Wakes me up.)

Then walk five blocks out of the way (the

walk will do you good) to the outdoor vegetable stand where you can take your time selecting the most glorious, flawless examples of these. Go to the best butcher in your neighborhood for good lean meats. Get the best hot and cold soups in the most expensive gourmet store around. Pay more. It will make everything taste better.

Now think of yourself as going on a health diet. Something you're gaining, not something you're giving up. Everything that enters your mouth will be giving you nourishment, will be a positive thing—you're not sacrificing anything. Complement the diet with eight hours sleep every night. (This is terribly important. So you won't rationalize stuffing your face with candy bars, telling yourself you need the quick energy because you're tired.) Take two of the one-a-day type vitamins every day. And keep aspirin on hand, because the first symptom of dieting is often a headache.

Eat as much as you like—of these thinning foods. No frying, please. No fats. No alcohol. No breads. (But put as much salt as you'd like on anything you like.) And I repeat: eat as much as you want. After a while you won't even be tempted when you pass the candy counter. It will make you a little queasy to see a fat girl eating pie. You'll feel so much better on this new regime that you probably won't ever revert to your former ways. You'll at last realize that *everyone*—even the skinny model—has to work at staying thin. But it's worth it. Today's woman doesn't go on diets—she never goes off one.

I'd stay away from the diet pills, but that's just me. I've read some reports that said all they do is psych you up. (And make doctors rich.) But if you need them, you need them. With me they are a false crutch. They gave me this false energy so I would run around like sixty all day, thinking I was "accomplishing," but the things I accomplished were accomplished a little hysterically, if you know what I mean. And at night I was bitchy. And I couldn't sleep. When I went off them I was exhausted for days. But it's up to you.

If you really have a problem (I'd consider anything over fifteen extra pounds a problem), see a doctor.

n Exercise

◆ My friend Norma came to New York full of beans, straight from college, where she had been the captain of the hockey team, had taken six hours of modern dance a week, and had walked over two miles a day just getting from class to class. She was in fine physical shape. She immediately got a job as a receptionist in one of New York's finest publishing houses—and almost as immediately forgot about exercising.

Three and a half years later, from Monday through Friday, nine to five, she was sitting at that very same reception desk. Three and a half years later! She had long since stopped smiling at the creative types who stepped off the elevator, however. In fact, the wait from lunch to five was becoming increasingly intolerable. At five she got to go home.

But five would come and she was still bored. She tried hard to drown this boredom with frantic excitement, began the nightly routine of discothèque-hopping. Every night a new man too. Soon she tired of that as well. She felt she was becoming jaded, sophisticated. In desperation she began reading those "woman" books— you know? The ones that solve all your problems? They didn't work either. She was on the very verge of giving up and going back home to Ohio where she belonged . . .

When one day a friend asked if she'd like to go horseback riding in Central Park the following morning. She said sure. And she went. She loved it. Not much time passed before it became a three-times-a-week thing.

First thing she knew she began to enjoy New York. She wasn't always tired any more. And maybe it was coincidence, but in two months' time she was promoted to researcher. Now she's an editor. Exercise isn't only good for the body, you know. It keeps your mind alert too.

Of course, to begin with a sport like Norma did is ideal. But Norma is independently wealthy. We're not. And horseback riding means money. In New York it's $5 an hour during the week, $6 on week-ends. Tennis is almost a physical impossibility. You have to have very blue blood indeed to get into those snobby tennis clubs. And if your blood isn't that bloody blue, or your wallet that awfully full, it's a bore to wait in line at the two few public courts. Golf? Don't be ridiculous. Even swimming is difficult unless you plan your swims around your shampoos.

So I'd say that sports are an impractical luxury. They're certainly more fun than daily deep-knee bends, but at the mercy of so many other influences. Like money, or weather, or other people.

Exercise, however, is up to you. If you want to exercise, you can, whatever the outside influences may happen to be. The perennial problem is wanting to. It's easy to want to play tennis. But wanting to touch your toes? Come on . . .

I lie to myself. I turn on the Beatles, or the Rolling Stones, or Trini Lopez very loud, and I pretend I'm just going to dance. (I love to dance.) Then I do my exercises with a little Martha Graham thrown in.

It's easy to lie to yourself for thirty minutes out of the day. It's even easier if you split it into two fifteen-minute parts. (Exercise does all the right things at the right times—it wakes me up in the morning and tires me out at night.)

Consistency is the thing here. You've got to do it every day, or don't bother—you'll only get stiff. It's a good idea to exercise for approximately the same length of time, at approximately the same time of day, every day. Like brushing your teeth. Otherwise you forget.

And you have got to mean it. If you just go

through the motions, you're wasting your time. Exercise has to be vigorous. When you swing your leg, swing so it pulls. So it hurts. If you don't particularly feel the swing, nothing much is happening to that leg.

◆ The exercises you choose are up to you. There are different ones for all the different body areas. I begin with the general exercises for allover energy, like the knee bends, the hip sways, or touching the toes, and running in place.

My specific problem is hips and thighs. The "fanny walk" is fabulous for fannies. Sit down, and with hands on hips, walk across the room using the cheeks of your buttocks as legs. Pull with the waist. Cross the room four or five a day (depending on the size of the room), and the rolls will start rolling away. Guaranteed. There's another I call the "thigh roll," which also involves sitting down. This time place your hands on the floor at your sides for support, bend your knees, keeping the feet on the floor, and with your thighs together, start rolling them from side to side, touching the floor each time. Do that twenty times a day. The best one for the stomach muscles is lying flat, hands behind your head, with legs stretched out straight ahead, ten inches above the floor. I don't know the name of that one. Let's call it the "ten-inch lie-flat." My favorite exercise of all, the "waist swing," slims the waist. I don't have a waist problem—I do it for fun. It's great with music. All you do is stand, feet apart, with your arms at shoulder level. Then, moving from the waist only, swing your arms around to the far right, then to the far left, and so on. If you follow your hands with your eyes, it prevents your chin from sagging, besides. It's a wonderful way to wake up in the morning.

Some people like to make charts and things like that. I don't happen to be one of them, but if you are, and if it gives you a little added incentive, then do. Every little bit helps.

So much for the formal exercising. Equally significant is what I call "informal exercising." You should be "informally exercising" every waking moment of the day. It has to do with constant unconscious attention to your body. Some people call it posture, but I think it's more than that. Sitting, with your head held high, is good for the whole upper half of the body. While you're cleaning out the tub you're stretching your torso. That sort of thing. What it is is really doing what you're doing. If you're walking, really walk. If you're sitting, sit—don't lounge. If you're lounging, you should be relaxing. Otherwise sit. That kind of thing. It's just doing whatever you're doing all the way.

9

n Travel

◆ Have toothbrush, will travel . . .

Let's face it, anything involving a toothbrush and a fresh set of underwear is traveling. You can "travel" ten blocks to spend the night with your beau, or you can travel around the world for a year. Basically it's all the same. You have to look fabulous. But looking fabulous without all the conveniences of home requires some planning.

Sometimes, though, forethought is impossible. Overnight travel is often—umm, spontaneous. Sometimes you haven't the time or the inclination to go home and grab your toothbrush and clean underpants. Sometimes things just happen. And you find yourself spending the night at someone else's apartment. Well, it does happen, and I think it's dumb not to admit it. And it's even more dumb not to be ready for it when it does happen.

The solution to the unexpected overnight "trip" is to always be prepared. Carry many of the absolute essentials in your purse. And keep the rest in your office drawer. Your purse should house foundation, an eyebrow pencil, eye liner and brush, pressed powder, mascara, lip gloss, and a small hairbrush. Always. You can keep some paste foundation in a small pillbox (the creamy stuff leaks). Your eyebrow pencil, in emergency, doubles as eye shadow. (Just put it on very lightly and smear it in with your finger.) The eye-liner brush should have a cover so it doesn't get monched. The rest is self-explanatory. The desk drawer at the office holds everything else you could ever ask for—fresh pants, deodorant, toothbrush, Tampax, astringent, Coets, hair spray, and cologne.

◆ Weekends are more like vacations than the spur-of-the-moment overnight jaunts. They involve suitcases. And once you've got a suitcase, you're expected to be ready for anything. So be ready for anything. Clothes aside, every suitcase should have: aspirin, Tums, Kleenex, Tampax, small soap, washcloth and hand towel, shower cap, deodorant, dusting powder, cologne, toothbrush, toothpaste, dental floss, hairbrush, comb, 5 or 6 rollers, bobby pins, 1 barrette, small can hair spray, nail brush, emery board, small tube hand cream, toenail clipper, headband, small plastic bottle of astringent, Coets, Q-tips, moisturizer, tweezers, eye drops, small sewing kit with scissors, 2 safety pins, small travel razor, rubber thong sandals, travel alarm clock, and a book to read.

That's clothes aside. The list may seem ridiculously long to you now, but wait, just wait until that Saturday night you're stuck up in Vermont somewhere, twenty miles from the nearest drugstore, and you have this hangnail. Or your skirt hem comes out when you step into it (you should never step into a skirt, by the way), or one of the buttons on his jacket comes off. If you haven't a needle and thread, no one else will. No one else ever does.

All of the above, except for the book, can just stay there in the suitcase until the next trip. (Most of them fit neatly into one of those convenient cosmetic "travel kits.") The book is the only last-minute item thus mentioned. (For me it's a guaranteed good time. It's like carrying an umbrella. If I don't bring one, I'm inevitably bored to tears. If I bring one, there's never a minute to read it.)

You want to know why Sam finally proposed? He told me I'm the only girl he knew he could be with, get the urge to go somewhere with, and just "take off," without the whole "preparation ordeal." Even now that I have the security of the wedding ring, I can pack for a weekend in less than ten minutes.

◈ There are a few basic clothes that should always go into a suitcase (and certain things you don't have to bring). A nightgown, of course, is a must. And even for a weekend five pairs of underpants isn't a bad idea. You never need a bathrobe—it takes up too much room. Use your coat. And you don't need slippers—you have those rubber thongs. A sweater is usually handy, even in summer. And a plain black silk sleeveless dress can go anywhere.

I would say that weekends are as difficult to pack for as long vacations. When I went for that trip around the world, I went tourist class, which meant forty pounds of luggage or less. Every time I went out for dinner I wore my black sleeveless dress—in Japan, where it was winter, as well as in Ceylon, where it was hot. Everywhere. Every time. Tank tops, sweaters, and skirts took care of the days. Three pairs of shoes —black silk, black sexy leathers, and brown clodhoppers. No problem. But on weekends you might want to go riding, which means at least blue jeans and some heavy shoes with a heel if you don't have boots, or go swimming, which means a bathing suit and a big towel, etc., etc. No telling what you'll be doing on a weekend.

You can pretty well pre-plan a vacation, however. Ask yourself these questions. What kind of weather can you expect where you're going? What kind of people? How long does it take to get there? How are you getting there? Are you traveling alone? If not, is your traveling companion a man or a woman? Are you going for work or pleasure? What are you going to do when you get there? How long will you be away? How many different stops will you make?

These questions are not as obvious as you might think. A few Easters ago I made the mistake of arriving in Nice ready for Nantucket. I felt pretty dowdy there, among all those Chanel suits.

It's impossible to make a set of wardrobe rules. My sister went to Rome two weeks after I returned last year, and she didn't dress anything the way I did. She was on the Via Veneto all the time and in fancy restaurants. I was out in the slums taking pictures. Same time of year exactly, but two entirely different wardrobes. Skirts, sweaters, and my boring beige raincoat (it's not really boring—it's fabulous) stood me in good stead. Sandie, on the other hand, needed silks and satins and things. So what you hope to do once you arrive is an important question.

10

n Time

◈ Cathie would come home from work nights, without anything to do, or so she thought, plunk herself down on the bed, and start dialing. She'd begin with "A" and keep on dialing every number in her address book until she got an answer. It didn't matter who answered—anyone would do. A "connection." Then she'd chat with whoever it was who by now regretted answering the ring, until finally she'd hear, "Gee, Cathie, thanks for calling. We'll have to get together sometime. Why don't you give me a call at the end of next week?" If that connection was listed at the bottom of page "P," she'd begin all over again with the "Q's" if she knew any "Q's"; anyway, she knew a lot of "R's." And one of her "S's" was sure to be home.

She spent on the average of four nights a week like that—talking with anyone who would listen—filling the empty hours until it was time to go to sleep.

But the fact is, Cathie's apartment was not-to-be-believed messy. And her hair was almost always greasy. And she hemmed her skirts with Scotch tape. And she wore dirty stockings a lot because she never seemed to have a clean pair.

I think maybe the reason why this kind of thing happened is that she thought of one evening as all evenings. "I'm alone tonight. No one wants to spend tonight with me. Therefore I am going to grow old alone. I am unloved, unneeded, unappreciated," etc. If she could take it for what it is, an evening alone—*an* evening alone—she would probably have used it as an opportunity to get herself a little organized. Biting off all of life is impossible to chew.

One night I was Cathie's connection. She started whining about her job that was boring, her boy friend who had given her up, her parents who had raised her all wrong, her psychiatrist who was "helping her," but even so she didn't have anything to do now that Don had dumped her. By this time it was 11:30.

I said, "Cathie, how long has it been since you've washed your hair?"

"Umm, a little over a week, I guess."

"Why don't you hang up the phone right now and wash your hair?"

"Oh, what's the use? Why even bother? I won't be seeing Don tomorrow, anyway."

"Do you wash your hair for Don?"

"Yes, of course."

"You're kidding. Doesn't your scalp itch if you wait too long?"

"Well, yes."

"Cathie"—I changed the subject—"what are you going to wear tomorrow?"

"Oh, I don't know. I hadn't thought about it. Why?"

"I just wondered. Do you have anything that you'd really like to wear tomorrow?"

"Not really."

"Well, do you have anything that fits you really well? I mean, do you have just one dress that's the right length?"

"No. That's the trouble. I haven't any clothes. And I don't have any money to go out and buy any, either."

"Why haven't you any money? You make a good salary, and your apartment's cheap. What do you spend it on?"

"Well, living is awfully expensive, you know. Just the basics are unbelievable."

"What basics?"

"Well, the telephone, for instance. Do you know that my bill this month is seventy-five dollars?"

"Seventy-five dollars! Why? Mine is twenty dollars this month and I thought that was bad. Who have you been calling?"

"Well, my brother's in Los Angeles—I've called him a couple of times. And I have this friend in New Haven I call whenever I'm a little down."

"Why don't you try letters?"

"Oh, I can't be bothered with letters. When I get the urge to speak with someone, I want to speak to them right then. I don't want to wait two weeks for an answer."

"Oh . . . Well, listen, Cathie, I've got to go now. Why don't you give me a call toward the end of next week? Maybe we can get together. Okay?"

◈ There's a little Cathie in all of us. The thing to do is to lick it. Time is the most beautiful gift we have, and we don't know how much of it we were given. So there's no excuse, if you think about it, to waste the smallest amount of it on self-pity.

What do you want to do with your time? Nothing is too grand as far as I'm concerned. As soon as I finish this book I'm going to make a movie. Me, make a movie! I don't even know what a movie camera looks like. But I'm going to learn. That's my next project. (So if you hear of a movie directed and photographed by Barbara Waterston in the next couple of years, I'd appreciate your going to have a look.)

Once you've made the big decision not to waste your time wondering and worrying, don't go the way of Gloria, either. Gloria was going to paint. She was the next Picasso—there wasn't a doubt in her mind. She painted every free minute she had.

But in order to pay for her supplies, and to pay the rent, she had to keep a nine-to-five job. As soon as she'd get home from the office she'd begin to paint, and she'd paint right through until after midnight, when she'd go to bed. Pretty soon she had paint on all her skirts, three of her office dresses, her one winter coat, and a big smudge of ochre on her sofa. All her dishes had a small film of turpentine on them. And speaking of greasy hair . . . And talk about dirty finger-nails . . .

Eventually she lost her job, of course. Which kept her from painting because she couldn't afford canvases until she got another one. If Gloria had spent two of her evenings a week taking care of her apartment, her clothes and herself, she would have been left with five nights that were really free. She could so easily have taken her clothes off when she returned from the office, hung them up, and put on a smock. But no, she was an *artiste*, and artists don't care about the way they live; they care only about their painting.

Well, have you ever seen photographs of Picasso's studio? It's in better shape than most living rooms. Everything is neat and clean and where it belongs. You can be sure when Picasso wants a certain brush he knows where to look for it and it's going to be clean once he finds it.

Organization is not confining—it's freedom! After your own house is in order you can concentrate on other things. But only after. Otherwise—in the back of your mind, at least—you're wondering when you're going to get the chance to do the things that have to be done. Checkbooks have to be balanced, and bills must be paid, and it's silly not to face that.

That whole "dumb blonde" bit is done with anyway. "Vague" doesn't have anything to do with "feminine"any more. (My theory on the matter is that it was the same men who insisted on marrying virgins who went for the dumb blondes. What if a better lover had gotten there first, right? Otherwise, why the big deal? I ask myself.) The dumb ones are still easier to handle —no threats, no problems. But most men find them boring nowadays, thank God. The men I've talked to, anyway.

Schedules are made to be broken, granted. I want you organized, not rigid. But any schedule is better than no schedule. A schedule is a plan. And plans imply activity. And activity is what we're here for, after all.

The schedule I have to break sometimes is simply that on Monday and Thursday nights I put my house in order. That leaves me with five nights to party, to read, to go to the movies, to go away, to do whatever I want to do. Two nights of reality to five of fancy isn't too tough a pill to swallow.

n Money

◆ Five years ago, when I was about to step into the New York Career Girl thing, my aunt sat me down and helped me work out a working budget. My take-home pay was $59.00 a week. Here it is:

Rent	$14.00
Food	10.00
Savings	5.50
Clothes	5.00
Entertainment	5.00
Transportation	4.00
Miscellaneous	4.00
Doctors	3.00
Dentists	3.00
Phone	2.50
Con Edison	1.50
Cleaning and laundry . . .	1.50

Well, that's fine for reasonable people, but I was a little too young for reason. Five dollars a week for clothes barely keeps you in stockings! Once every two months you get to buy a dress? That's six a year. No haircuts ever? Forget it. Do all your own laundering so you can have one dress cleaned a week? No! There is a way out of this mess, but it means cutting a couple of corners.

First corner to cut, I'd say, would be savings. We're not going to concern ourselves with the future, are we? The future we're after is *him*. And we're not going to get him by spending $5 a week on clothes. If "him" turns out to be some gorgeous but starving artist, *then* save. You'll have a lifetime to save. First things first.

Okay, now we're up to $10.50 for clothes.

Now what about these doctors? Three dollars a week? I've been to the doctor exactly four times in the last five years (and one time was for a blood test!) at $10 a try. That's $40 total for doctors in five years. If I had saved my $3 a week for doctors I'd have probably run to him every time I had a headache. Three dollars a week for five years is $780 to spend on clothes.

So you're up to $13.50.

Dentists? Better save. A crown is $75 minimum.

But $10 a week on food? Really. Maybe in the beginning, until everything starts working, but in no time you'll be taken to dinner as often as you're free. The nights you spend at home have yogurt.

Even when your date would rather take you to a bar than to dinner (and I don't blame him), if he tries to push another drink down you (and he probably will—in hopes of putting you in a receptive frame of mind, so to speak), ask for a hamburger "instead," not "too." And there you have another meal under your belt.

Have lunch with all the men you turn down for nights because five hours with them seems intolerable. Remember, lunch is only an hour. And it's a meal. On the days no one bites for lunch, bring some fresh fruit to the office. Don't forget to do this. I gained fifteen pounds in the first three months of my first office job because when lunch time came I'd order a sandwich. With lots of mayonnaise because I hate "dry" sandwiches.

So all the food you have to buy is grapefruit for breakfast, fruits for lunch, yogurt for the nights you're at home, and a very occasional lamb chop. Don't learn to cook—you'll have plenty of time for that later on. Keeping a well-stocked kitchen costs a minimum of $15 a week. Wait until after your raise.

You may have noticed I didn't mention your apartment here. I feel the same about apartments as I do about food. Sure, nice to have a lovely apartment, and sure, lovely to have a well-stocked kitchen. But first things first. After the raise.

Chances are you have a roommate or two, anyway. And that, more often than not, means full-time mess. So make a deal with her (or them)—let them blame the mess on you with their friends, so you can blame the mess on them with yours. If you live alone, which of course is ideal, then your raise has probably already come through.

Anyway, five of that $10 for food goes for clothes. We're up to $18.50 a week.

How about this entertainment? Let them take you to the movies. And if you spend an evening with a girl friend, go over to her house and watch the tube. Or have her to yours for a chat.

You now have $23.50 a week for clothes.

And what, after all, is miscellaneous? I'd call it clothes. Do you realize that you have $27.50 a week to spend on clothes? That's way over $100 a month! That's over $1200 a year!!

Now when I say "clothes," don't take me at my absolute word. I mean "you." Haircuts, cosmetics, *and* clothes. You can make the best-dressed list on $1,200 a year.

12

On the Hows and Whys

◈ Why bother? Why not?

Beauty is beautiful, let's face it. Otherwise why have artists been wasting their time for all these centuries? Beauty is uplifting. When I see a greasy-faced, greasy-haired girl walking down the street I feel a little squirmy. I imagine my scalp is itching. But if I see a freshly scrubbed young thing, all clean and neat, I feel uplifted, just as a smile is always more uplifting than a frown.

You're right, of course—it hasn't anything to do with the "real" issues. Whether your hair is straight or curly doesn't solve the Vietnam problem. Wearing your skirts short doesn't make you a better physicist, if that's what you are. Great shoes are not going to make you a great lover or even a great secretary. Pulling yourself together doesn't in itself make you anything.

But what it does do is this: it frees you to become anything. When you're talking to your boss, you're not half listening and at the same time half hoping he doesn't notice the spot on your collar. When you're with your banker beau who is explaining investing, you're actually learning something of what Wall Street is about; you're not wondering if he likes your new "Mod" dress or wishing your hair were clean. Two nights a week of setting yourself straight leaves you with five nights and seven days to become whatever it is you're becoming.

Now that I'm working free-lance, it's easy to let myself go, especially if I haven't any appointments during a particular day. On several different mornings during the writing of this book, for example, I began to work without getting myself in shape first, sort of half in my nightgown with my hair uncombed. I was working at home, so I thought it didn't matter. But I found it did matter. I couldn't think clearly. In the back of my head there was always the unmade bed and the shopping which had to be done. It's like when I was at college, before every exam I'd put on a fresh blouse and skirt and get my room in shape; I'd go to the exam "pulled together." Once there, I found it was easier to pull my thoughts together as well. Organization helps my concentration.

Just getting pulled together is a victory in itself. Simply having a freshly pressed dress and clean underwear to wear in the morning requires a somewhat orderly mind.

But I hope I'm making myself clear—the whole point is so you can dismiss it. If you wear dirty stockings to the office, you're thinking about them all morning. And then you waste twenty minutes of your lunch hour running to the drugstore for a new pair. Why should you be thinking about stockings (or the safety pin in your skirt) for three hours of your day? You shouldn't. It bogs you down.

Keeping up with the current fashions is worth while for the same reason—so you can dismiss them. Wondering if what you are wearing makes it or misses is as distracting as dirty stockings. It keeps your mind from what it should be on. How do you know if what you're wearing misses or not, unless you *know?* You know? Otherwise you just hope. And hoping is only a better way of wondering than doubting. It's not like knowing.

◆ It all goes back to that full-length mirror, without which there isn't even any hope. You have to see yourself to know yourself. Only then can you make an intelligent decision as to what's going to work for you. Like I have a good figure; everyone agrees. But I know that my legs are too short for the rest of me. That's why I wear my skirts short—because my legs look longer with short skirts. And that's why I don't wear pants. But that doesn't mean I don't like pants on Jean Shrimpton. She has long legs.

(Pants suits are another matter, however. A great pants suit has a great long jacket that covers the rear, so it looks like your legs start higher up than they really do.)

Only you can make your decisions. Not your boyfriend, or your girl friend, or your mother, or me. I may tell you that lipstick is the pits and why I think so. But if you still like you with lipstick after you've really thought about it, really looked in the mirror, then I like you for your decision.

If *you* decide on it, then anything you do, anything you wear, is not going to miss. So many women these days don't want to take the responsibility for their decisions, so they do exactly what the fashion magazines tell them to do. They think they can go into a store and, if they pay enough money, they can buy *chic*. Buy dignity. They forget that they have to wear what they buy.

And only you can wear your clothes. If you buy a dress, fabulous though it may be, even if it was on the cover of *Vogue*, you're going to wind up looking silly if it looks like the cover of *Vogue* and not YOU.

After you know who you are and what you can handle, you can dress well. Until then you're walking around wearing somebody else's decision. Gloria Steinem, one of the chicest young things in New York, wrote in *Glamour* a few years back, "Don't borrow, steal . . . Make it yours!"

I think she had the right idea. If you see some

111

fabulous new something at a cocktail party or on the street, be it a hairdo, a way of wearing a scarf, a pair of sunglasses, or a kind of shoe, sure, run and buy that shoe, tie that scarf, or get those glasses. But adapt them to *you*. Make them yours!

It's that whole instant-coffee, instant-chic thing I was talking about in Chapter Three. There's no way of having a "look" until you have a "self." And you aren't a person until you have some opinions, so you're not going to have a look until you can make your own decisions. Sorry. There's no shortcut. (I think it's ironic that I'm writing a "How To" book, because I believe so strongly that no one—not me or anyone else—can tell you "how to" anything.)

You've got to remember that fashion is business. The reason manufacturers come out with "pastels for fall" or other such dogmas is to make themselves a bit of cash. That's why. Some Seventh Avenue manufacturer isn't going to be able to cash in on your indecision if you make your decisions. How do they know what looks well on you? What do I know? Nothing.

When you start making your own decisions, you're not going to fall prey to every passing foolish fad. You'll spot the trends, go with them, and leave the fads behind. The difference between trends and fads is simply that trends usually have a reason behind them. Fads don't. Fads are just someone's fancy. Like the reason for short, waistless shifts is that they allow for greater freedom, thus more action. It's easier to take longer steps in shorter dresses. And, as I said before, they make your legs look longer. The reason the bustle was dropped is that it was just so much excess garbage. Today's fast pace doesn't allow for *any* excess baggage, be it five too many pounds of flesh or five too many yards of fabric. Watch proportions. Proportions are trends.

So now that you've given it some thought and you have a look that looks like you, now that you're all pulled together, forget it! Let your hair down. It's like money—if your new-found beauty starts meaning anything more than freedom, it's ugly.

13

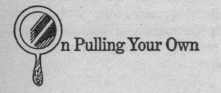n Pulling Your Own

◆ When I was in the fifth grade, I went to see this Van Johnson movie. The opening scene showed Van Johnson sitting all alone in some outdoor café in some European city (I was only in the fifth grade) and he spotted some ex-general and his wife walking toward him. The three of them began to talk, and the ex-general (I'm not entirely sure he was an ex-general—maybe he was just a sergeant) made some smart-guy remark like, "Ha, ha, remember when you came to me asking permission to marry that girl?"

And Van Johnson didn't think that was such a joke. What I've told you so far took place after the war—let's say three or four years after the war. Now there's this flashback and we see old

Van in bed or some sensitive place with this frightened girl, see. And they are in love. You get that immediately. But the girl is very afraid of life and things in general. And old Van, to make her happy, and himself happy, too—I must admit that because they really are in love—proposes. They are to get married the next day. (Actually there were a whole lot of sensitive scenes before they decide to get married, because it's a full-length movie.)

So the next day he tries to get permission to marry her, and here's where the big-shot sarge comes in—he won't grant the permission. And then, for some strange reason, Van gets picked up and put in jail. He tries to explain that he's got to get to this girl because he was supposed to marry her and she'll be very upset. Finally he convinces some tough jail-keeper type to call and tell her that he couldn't get there. So the next scene is this jail keeper on the phone with the sensitive girl and he's saying, "Look, lady, I don't know. He just told me to tell you the wedding's off and he can't make it."

The last scene is back in that café in—let's call it Paris, and the big-shot sergeant is still laughing, and he says, "What ever happened to that girl, anyway?" And Van Johnson says, "They found her in the river three days later."

And you'd better believe that movie got me where I live. Wow. Oh, tragedy, she was so beautiful! And she killed herself! For him! For Van Johnson. And if Van Johnson loved her, then that must be what's feminine.

◆ That was my first lesson in "femininity." I've had a million others since. But all the lessons teach me is that being feminine is being negative. A female-female is always a little confused— that's appealing. She's weak so the man can feel strong. She's dependent so she won't get out of hand. She's submissive so he can be aggressive. He Tarzan, she Jane.

A man is supposed to be strong so a woman, to "complement" him, to "complete" him, has to be the opposite. To be really feminine, you have to be everything he isn't. (And if he's a great guy, you're in trouble.)

And a woman isn't ever a woman until she's with a man; after all, didn't she get her backbone from one of his ribs, or something? A man can be a man by himself, but a woman isn't even a person until she belongs to a man. That's what my lessons taught me. I got them from all over— from more movies, novels, my parents, my friends—everyone (*anyone*) else could tell me how to be "feminine" better than I could tell myself.

It was okay for me to have my "career" before my white knight happened along, as long as I realized I was only biding my time. But when he did perchance to arrive, especially after I had won my hard-earned title "wife," I did what I always knew I would do—I stopped to become his "other half."

I not only quit my job—my fabulous job—I quit wearing my skirts short (I was a wife now, and "wives" are conservative). And at parties I'd stand by his side and smile a lot—that was feminine. (Me! I was voted class flirt in high school!)

When I got married I stopped everything. I stopped having opinions—I was only the wife. The husband has the opinions. I had a husband who would take care of me now, so I *could* stop. My husband would support me in every way. He had to. He was my legal husband. What I stopped being was the girl he had fallen in love with—that's what I stopped being. I wasn't fun any more. I was a drag. I had stopped being an adult. I was right back to the all-take relationship I had with my mother when I was a child. I was a parasite. I wasn't pulling my own.

I don't know why so many of us fall into that rut. Why do we want to "belong" to someone? Why must we be possessed? "Owned." It's like I used to love my dog. She was always there waiting for me to come home. Wagging her tail. Waiting. Ready to lick me and let me love her. But she wasn't any challenge. There wasn't any "friction." She never disagreed with me; she was always grateful for the tiniest of attention. For the very crumbs from my table. She was a pleasure to have around the house, sure, but she wasn't awfully stimulating. She certainly didn't make me grow. We never shared anything . . .

Then one morning came the dawn. I was being Sam's adorable little puppy. Sure, he'd pet me when he thought of it. But he wasn't becoming a bigger man for knowing me; in fact, he was growing worse because with me he felt guilty for not wanting to pet me as often as I wanted him to (which was all the time—I had nothing else to do). Yes, master! Wag. Wag. Feed me, please! I *beg* of you! I'm so hungry! Oh, my beautiful master, aren't you kind, you tousled my hair just then. Thank you! Thank you!

That's fine for dogs. But we're people. People have brains. And people with brains have minds of their own. They have opinions. Maybe squashing your opinions makes for more peace, but that's peace at an awful price. Peace paid for by your self-respect. Peace built on a lie.

◈ I know I'm not alone here. Most of my friends, in fact, have fallen into this rut of "femininity." Maybe it's because we all think that "femininity" is the same thing as "sexy." I don't think it is any more. I tried it. I went through that submissive routine, but Sam didn't think I was so sexy. In fact, I think he was rather bored.

Sexiness is directed from the inside, out. "Sexy" is sexless. What do we all find irresistibly sexy about men? A sense of humor, a twinkle in the eye—unbelievably sexy. The same things are "sexy" in women. Show me a man who loves being alive, and I'll show you my idea of sexy. And a woman who loves being alive is just as sexy. Energy's sexy. Zest. Vigor. That's sexy. Sexiness is "What can I give?" Doggy femininity is "What can I get?" There's a lot of difference there.

118

Let's face it, for the sex act to work, there has to be a certain amount of friction. Without it there's no pleasure, no pain, nothing. Well, I think this is true with relationships too. If there isn't any resistance, then nothing's *happening*.

Peter, a friend of ours, is now in the process of getting a divorce from Anne. He says it's because of lack of communication. Anne was so flabby "feminine" that she never gave Peter any resistance. His word was unquestioned dogma. Anne has never disagreed with him once in their three years of married life. Anne's only interest in life was Peter. Pleasing Peter. Poor Peter would say something to her, wanting a reaction, wanting to hear what she thought, and inevitably he'd discover, and rediscover, that she hadn't any thoughts. She just agreed. So Peter, to reach her, started making more and more outrageous remarks. React! Please, Anne, say *something!* But Anne just wanted to please him, so she couldn't react; she had nothing to draw from but him. She wasn't a person—she was just a part of him. There wasn't any friction. He wasn't getting anything back. He wasn't being effective with her (how can you have an effect on a non-person) and he wasn't being affected by her. So he got a reaction from his secretary one day, and you know the rest . . .

◆ You may think I'm talking a lot about marriage, but I'm really talking about relationships (marriage is just a relationship). Marriage is where I learned to relate to a person. I don't think I had any real relationships before then. I was always relating to an image, or to an idea of what other people thought I should be like, never actually to another person. They couldn't reach me because there wasn't anything there to reach.

Let me give you an example. When I was in college I went to a football game with a boyfriend and a married couple (friends of his). I was very shy then, so all during the game I didn't speak unless spoken to. After the game we went to some restaurant for dinner, and the married man turned to me and said, "What's with you? Don't you like us?" And I, taken aback, said, "Oh yes! Yes! [or something] I think you're all great. I'm just afraid you don't like me!"

And this guy said, "If you *really* liked us, you wouldn't concern yourself with how we felt about you. You'd be too busy liking us."

And he was right—I know he was. If I had been thinking of how I could add to the day, instead of taking from it, it would have been more pleasant all around. But I was too concerned about the impression *I* was making to care about them.

I didn't have any self-respect then. I didn't have any sense of myself—of who I was, or what I had to offer. How can you give to someone if you don't think you have anything that's worth giving? You can't. I couldn't.

But self-respect is difficult to come by. It goes against everything we've learned since we were tiny children. Everything I ever did was for someone else's approval. I cleaned up my room

120

so my mother would like me, not because I cared about having a clean room. I studied in school for the grade—the ultimate score. I'd cram, take the exam, and fifteen minutes later forget everything. It had nothing to do with learning. The mark was the thing that mattered.

When I got to New York I'd try to please my various lady bosses. It didn't matter if *I* knew I was being lazy, so long as *they* didn't find out. When I went out on dates I'd change my character to fit the man. With one I'd be naïve and sensitive, with another I'd be blasé and sophisticated, with another I'd be tough and smart-alecky. I'd try to be each new boyfriend's idea of the "ideal mate."

I've always tried to be everybody else's ideal something-or-other. I had to be special because I wanted people to like me. But never (until I saw Sam was getting bored) did I ever even think to try pleasing myself. So I could hold my head up high and look people straight in the eye and say, "Hello. I'm me. That's what I am. Who are you?"

I think I was "buying" people then. "If I'm special enough, then you'll like me." I was very ambitious because I wanted a "title." That's Barbara. She's a fashion reporter. If people knew I was a fashion reporter, then they'd have to like me because that meant I was a big deal. I was all the right things for all the wrong reasons. I was polite so people would like me, not because I liked people. I didn't like people. They scared me.

And I don't think it was all my fault. I think the system's a little at fault too. Everything we learn is so negative. We're taught not to kill, not to steal, not to swear, not to lie, not to dishonor our fathers and mothers, not to commit adultery, not to covet our neighbor's wife, not not. If we don't do any of these uglies, then we'll be "social creatures." We'll "fit in." We'll be "well-adjusted." And if you're "well-adjusted," well, that's just IT.

I think if we had been shown as children that there were things *to* do, not just things *not* to do, then table manners and rules wouldn't have to be rammed down our throats. If we felt that we had some purpose, some tiny little reason for being here, then we'd have learned self-respect. And once we've learned that, then we can start caring about other people. Then we know we're not ugly inside; we have something to give.

◆ There's been a carload of books and magazine articles written about "The Woman Problem" in the past few years. Should a woman get out of the kitchen and into the office, or should she stay at home where she belongs, or does she, indeed, belong there? And so on. Everybody's got an answer.

But there isn't one answer that can cover the massive word "Woman." No one would even try to generalize that way about "People." And that, of course, is what the problem really is—it's "The People Problem." Phyllis Batelle talks about the "non-woman," the "neuter-woman."

Betty Freidan tells women how to fulfill themselves. Michael Drury (who's a she, by the way) tells us how to love. Not to mention "Dear Abby" and all of those. But all any of them is saying is what *she* did. What *her* answer is.

Me? Yes, I have a career. I probably always will, though I don't know. I haven't any children yet, and I'll have to see how I feel when I do.

But that doesn't mean I think Sharon should have a career. Sharon hated her work in New York, and now that she's a mother and a wife, she's not only much happier, but she's found her special way of giving. Her child is beautiful; her husband is a much bigger person for being married to her, and so is Sharon. Sharon would be an idiot to go out again into the business world. That's not her particular bit. Her "career" is managing her house and giving to her family. She's not a parasite. This is her way of *giving*.

The same with Nancy. Nancy was a magazine editor until a month before the baby came, and then she left. Christina, her girl, is almost two now, and she is walking testimony of how Nancy has not been looking for "fulfillment" but has been looking to "give." Christina could read seven words (*toes*, *nose*, *arms*, *chair*, *Mommy*, *Daddy* and *table*) at nineteen months. Christina calls me "Barbar" and remembered me after her three-month summer in Europe. Christina already likes people—she really *likes* people. And she's only two years old!

Obviously Nancy hasn't been wasting her time. But Janet, another friend, the mother of

123

three, is. Those children drive her nuts. Constantly nagging, questioning, whining, wetting. Janet's at her wit's end by ten-thirty in the morning. Janet ought to get out of the house. It's not in her physical and emotional makeup to hang around the apartment answering questions and cleaning up all day long. She doesn't feel she's using what she has to offer the world. Probably if Janet had a career that she really loved and had something to give to, she would be more mellow come five-thirty when she got back to the apartment. And the fewer hours she spent with her children woud be more beneficial and more pleasant for everyone concerned.

◈ I don't think there's one answer for all women. And I think the reason these books and articles have so many avid readers is that damn "femininity" hang-up. We all think we should be something that we're not—otherwise we're "non-women." Why don't we concern ourselves more with the "Person" hang-up? Why don't we realize that if we don't make our own decisions we're being "non-people"?

Whenever I read another of those articles, a song I heard a long time ago begins coming back to me. It's from *Carnival*. Ta-dum-something about "justify the air I breathe and the space I take . . ." I haven't heard the song since, and it must have been five years ago. But I remember that line. I've got to justify the air I breathe and the space I take. That's so beautiful.

The fact is I was born with two arms and two

legs and eyes that see and ears that hear, in a country that taught me to read and write, and, well, I just wonder why—that's all. Why was I born in Boston and not Bombay? Why was I given a healthy body and a brain that works? Why can I smell? Why can I see and hear and taste? For my own pleasure? So I can wallow in my own enjoyment? I don't think so. I think I have to justify the air I breathe and the space I take.

And I don't think anyone else can tell me how to do that. No one knows what I have to offer better than I do. I listened to the others, all those voices, all those people who knew what I "should" be, and believe me, I was screwed up.

Now *I* decide. My husband doesn't tell me what I should be. No psychiatrist, no minister, no mother, no "Woman Problem" writer, no one else. *I* decide. Of course that's a little scary, because if I decide wrong, then there's no one else to blame. But I'm willing to risk that. If I fail, then I'll try another way.

This is where I stand this year. Next year I don't know where I'll be. Maybe I'm all wet this year. I'll have to see. *I'll* have to see.

SIGNET Books for Your Reference Shelf

SPECIALTY COOKING WITH WINE *by Morrison Wood*

The best of the world's most famous foods can now be prepared in your own kitchen. An expert shows how available ingredients are transformed into exotic fare by the creative use of American wines and liqueurs.
(#T2201—75¢)

GOURMET COOKING BY THE CLOCK *by William and Chesbrough Rayner*

An exciting new cookbook with step-by-step directions for gourmet meals that take as little as thirty minutes to prepare. (#T2221—75¢)

DYNAMIC SPEED READING *by Norman C. Maberly*

How to read up to ten times faster than the average reader, with greater understanding and enjoyment.
(#P2936—60¢)

SPEAK BETTER—WRITE BETTER—ENGLISH *by Horace Coon*

How to make words work for you. A practical reference book to increase your effectiveness in business and personal life. (#P2799—60¢)

HOW TO STUDY AND PREPARE FOR EXAMS *by Colin Woodley*

A comprehensive guide on how to study, do research, read and take notes . . . for all students in secondary school and college. With schedules, time-tables and aids for specialized studies. (#P2660—60¢)

THE NEW AMERICAN GUIDE TO COLLEGES, Revised and Enlarged *by Gene R. Hawes*

The only book that provides a statement of the admissions policies for all of the country's 2,168 colleges and universities, plus much useful information for the college-bound. Also contains a complete listing of graduate schools. (#Q2795—95¢)

A DICTIONARY OF AMERICAN-ENGLISH USAGE *by Margaret Nicholson*

A new version of Fowler's *Modern English Usage*, updated and geared to American usage. (#Q2632—95¢)

SIGNET Marriage and Health Manuals

AN ANALYSIS OF HUMAN SEXUAL RESPONSE *edited by Ruth and Edward Brecher*

A complete explanation for the layman of the controversial Masters-Johnson research on sexual response. Includes commentary by leaders in the study of sexual behavior, as well as prominent social critics.
(#T3038—75¢)

LOVE WITHOUT FEAR *by Dr. Eustace Chesser*

A noted physician and marriage counselor offers scientific information on how to achieve sex happiness in marriage. (#T3283—75¢)

PREGNANCY AND BIRTH *by Alan F. Guttmacher, M.D.*

A handbook for expectant parents by the Director of Gynecology and Obstetrics, Mount Sinai Hospital, New York. (#P2230—60¢)

101 INTIMATE SEXUAL PROBLEMS ANSWERED *by LeMon Clark, M.D.*

Drawing on his years of experience as physician, professor, and editor, LeMon Clark, M.D. provides straightforward answers to the questions men and women most often ask about sex. (#T3195—75¢)

THE NEW AMERICAN MEDICAL DICTIONARY AND HEALTH MANUAL *by Robert Rothenberg, M.D.*

Over 7500 definitions of medical terms, disorders, and diseases, with more than 300 illustrations, make this the most complete and easy-to-understand book of its kind. Also includes a comprehensive first-aid section and guides to better health. (#Q2038—95¢)

YOUR BODY AND YOUR MIND (Medicine for Moderns) *by Frank G. Slaughter, M.D.*

The famous doctor-novelist shows how emotions influence health and how anger, fear or worry can cause serious physical illness. (#P2302—60¢)

SIGNET Biographies You Will Enjoy Reading

GREAT STARS OF HOLLYWOOD'S GOLDEN AGE *edited by Frank C. Platt*

The true stories of the men and women behind the famous facades of Garbo, Valentino, Chaplin, Lombard, and John Barrymore. (#P2979—60¢)

JACQUELINE KENNEDY: A BIOGRAPHY *by Gordon Langley Hall and Ann Pinchot*

Anecdotes, photographs, and much personal information, some of it never before presented, reveal this extraordinary woman, from childhood through her days as First Lady. (#P2819—60¢)

LENA *by Lena Horne and Richard Schickel*

A great entertainer relates the dramatic story of her rise to stardom and her victory over fear and loneliness. (#T3015—75¢)

WHITE HOUSE NANNIE: My Years with Caroline and John Kennedy, Jr. *by Maud Shaw*

A warm personal view of an extraordinary family, written by a woman who lived with the Kennedys, sharing their joys and sorrows, for seven years. (#P3063—60¢)

THE WOMAN IN THE WHITE HOUSE *by Marianne Means*

The lives, times, and influence of twelve notable first ladies, from Martha Washington to Jacqueline Kennedy. (#T2512—75¢)

W. C. FIELDS: His Follies and Fortunes *by Robert Lewis Taylor*

A Pulitzer Prize-winning author chronicles the life of one of our century's funniest men, a man whose private adventures were no less hilarious than his masterful performances. Illustrated with photographs. (#Q3064—95¢)

BOGIE *by Joe Hyams*

The biography of Humphrey Bogart, a great star in his lifetime and now a cult hero for a whole generation who never saw his films while he was alive, written by a close friend of the star, with the authorization and cooperation of Bogart's widow. Introduction by Lauren Bacall. Thirty-two pages of photographs. (#T3071—75¢)